SOCIALISM

FOR BEGINNERS

ANNA PACZUSKA

ILLUSTRATED BY SOPHIE GRILLET

Writers and Readers

WRITERS & READERS in association with **UNWIN PAPERBACKS** London · Sydney

This edition first published by
Writers and Readers Publishing Cooperative
in association with
Unwin Paperbacks 1986

A *Writers and Readers* ➤ Documentary Comic Book © 1986

UNWIN ® PAPERBACKS
40 Museum Street, London WC1A 1LU, UK

Unwin Paperbacks
Park Lane, Hemel Hempstead, Herts HP2 4TE, UK

Writers and Readers Publishing Cooperative Society Limited
144 Camden High Street, London NW1 0NE, UK

Writers and Readers Publishing Inc.
500 Fifth Avenue, New York NY 10110

George Allen & Unwin Australia Pty Ltd
8 Napier Street, North Sydney, NSW 2060, Australia

Unwin Paperbacks with the Port Nicholson Press
PO Box 11—838, Wellington, New Zealand

Printed in Great Britain by
Richard Clay (The Chaucer Press) Ltd,
Bungay, Suffolk

ISBN 0 04 320194 6

Socialism
for
Beginners

by Anna Paczuska
with drawings by
Sophie Grillet

For JOEL, NADIA and PHIL

The seed ye sow, another reaps;
The wealth ye find, another keeps;
The robes ye weave, another wears,
The arms ye forge, another bears.

Sow seed – but let no tyrant reap;
Find wealth – let no impostor heap;
Weave robes – let not the idle wear;
Forge arms – in your defence to bear.
P B Shelley

Acknowledgements

Our thanks to Hal Draper whose pamphlet 'The Two Souls of Socialism' (International Socialists of America 1966) provided the inspiration for this book.

Also thanks to Ross Pritchard, Gerry Kelly, Phil Evans, Philip Boys, Mary Williams, Jonathan Neal, Enda O'Callaghan, Chloë Watkins, Bipin Patel and Olly Duke who made contributions and suggestions, and to Lin James who did the typesetting.

CONTENTS

SOCIALISM is simple. It is working-class men and women collectively and democratically running society for themselves. It is not a new idea. Most books say that socialism was conceived in France and Britain as recently as 1830, but that is only partly true. Ideas don't suddenly leap out of history fully formed. They grow from earlier ideas and are shaped by the society in which they develop. The vision of equality and co-operation which was called socialism in the early 1800s has been with us, in one form or another, for a very much longer time.

IT'S JUST AN **OUTDATED** 19th CENTURY IDEA

S.D.P.

SOCIALISM IS TOO **COMPLEX** FOR WORKERS TO UNDERSTAND

ACADEMIC

SOCIALISM MEANS **NO SEX** 'TILL YOU'RE 30

SOCIALISM IS JUST ANOTHER FORM OF PATRIARCHY

CAPITALISM IS THE EXPLOITATION OF MAN BY MAN — SOCIALISM IS THE OPPOSITE

CHINESE PEASANT

FEMINIST

EAST EUROPEAN WORKER

SOCIALISM IS DEATH TO THE LACKEYS OF IMPERIALISM!

3RD WORLD GUERILLA

As long as there has been class society, there have been rebellions. Throughout history people have fought injustice and inequality. Socialism is rooted in the age-old struggle for freedom and equality. Today the struggles against capitalism and imperialism continue that fight. All over the world there are socialists striving for equality and workers' power. But although more people than ever before call themselves socialists, they have all discovered socialism in a different way, and so have different ideas about what socialism is. An added complication is that many tyrannical regimes hide behind the name of socialism. And capitalists do everything they can to persuade everybody that tyranny – not freedom – is in the nature of socialism.

So socialism is at root a simple idea, but the word can have quite contradictory and confusing associations.

This book tells the story of socialism, how it grew out of the struggle for freedom, how it changed and how it has been misused. There is not room for everything, so as much space as possible has been devoted to the organization of the fight for freedom. Intellectuals have an important part to play, but ideas and theories are important only when they are born out of organization and struggle. In turn they help to stimulate and encourage new activity.

Many have dreamed about a world run by workers. Socialists go out and organize for it.

SOCIALISM IS HIGHER PRODUCTION NORMS

COMECON

RUSSIAN BUREAUCRAT

NO, NO! – YOU'VE ALL GOT IT WRONG!

LENIN

DO-IT-YOURSELF FREEDOM

SLAVE REVOLTS

The story begins with slave rebellions, of which there were many in the ancient world. The rebels were often joined by peasants and small tenant farmers, as well as by 'free' wage-workers (proletarians).

The most famous slave rebellion was led by **Spartacus**. It began in 73 BC when he and his fellow gladiators broke out of their barracks in Italy and called on other slaves to join them. Thousands came to their stronghold on the slopes of Mount Vesuvius. The slave armies easily defeated the hastily-gathered Roman regular troops sent to stop them. Women fought as fiercely as the men when the rebel camps were attacked. Soon the slave armies had marched the length of Italy undefeated.

SPARTACUS!
THE MOST SPLENDID FELLOW IN ALL ANCIENT HISTORY; A GREAT GENERAL, A NOBLE CHARACTER AND A REAL REPRESENTATIVE OF THE PROLETARIAT!

SHUCKS, KARL, YOU'RE MAKING ME BLUSH

9

Many of the slaves wanted to take on the power of Rome and defeat it – not just escape. Perhaps that is why when the way to the north and freedom lay open they turned back, to fight the Roman armies again. This time they were not successful. They were driven into the southern tip of Italy and finally defeated in a bloody battle in which many were killed, including Spartacus himself. Six thousand survivors were publicly crucified as an example to other slaves.

Even as the remnants of Spartacus's army cursed their murderers, 40,000 slaves in the mines of Spain, Delos and Macedonia were taking up arms. Fifty years later silver miners in Greece staged another massive insurrection. By the third century AD, Rome was threatened by rebellions in North Africa and all over the western part of its Empire.

An Arab writer described one African rising:

"They hate the master and the rich, and when they meet a master riding in his chariot and surrounded by his slaves, they make him get down, put the slaves in the chariot, and oblige their masters to run on foot. They boast that they have come to re-establish equality on earth, and they summon the slaves to liberty."

Empires that succeeded Rome suffered similar attacks. The Byzantine Empire was plagued by slave revolts and strikes. In the ninth century a rising of black slaves draining swamps in Egypt held out for fifteen years against their Arab rulers.

THE PEASANTS' REVOLT 1381

In the early 14th century, the Black Death swept Britain, killing a third of its inhabitants. It caused an acute labour shortage, and peasants saw their chance to demand better wages, an end to compulsory work on the manorial estates, lower rents and the right to move from job to job as they pleased, instead of being tied to one place for life.

The feudal lords resisted. In 1351 Parliament passed a Statute of Labourers which fixed wages at the levels prevailing before the plague, and forbade free movement. Lords returned to their old system of labour.

Peasants took direct action. Land leagues were formed, pledged to disobey bailiffs' orders. **John Ball** and other radical preachers urged the peasants on. Using well-known stories from the Bible to attack class inequalities, they spread their message across the country, regardless of threats to burn, brand and imprison them as 'reporters of horrible false lies concerning prelates, earls, barons and other nobles and great men of the realm'.

In 1381, when an extra tax was imposed, the peasants revolted. Commoners from Essex and Kent marched on London. At first their rising appeared to be successful. **King John** swiftly promised reforms and free pardons to all participants in the insurrection. Then their leader, **Wat Tyler**, was murdered by the Mayor of London as he came forward to parley with the Crown forces. Promises of reform were immediately revoked in Parliament and the peasant rebellion savagely crushed. Yet within twenty years the manorial system had virtually disappeared in Britain.

A rebellion was sparked off in Germany in 1525 when peasants rose in the Black Forest and Swabia and drew up a charter of twelve demands. These included abolition of serfdom, the right to hunt and cut wood in the forests, and the right to common grazing land, as well as religious freedoms within the Church

The best-organized rebellion, in Thuringia, was led by **Thomas Muntzer**. Like John Ball he used Bible stories to project his hatred of the rich. Nimrod, who had ordered the Tower of Babel to be built, was held to symbolize the ownership and control of private property. When Muntzer appealed to peasants to cast down 'Nimrod and his Tower', it was a clear call to insurrection.

Muntzer was finally captured. His back was broken on the rack. But killing individuals could not kill the ideals for which they fought.

LEVELLERS AND DIGGERS

Communistic ideas like Muntzer's reappeared during the English Revolution of the 1640s. All over Britain the common people were starving. Puritan and parliamentary forces successfully organised against the king. But killing the king was not in itself enough to break the power of the gentry. 'Levellers' wanted to take the revolution further.

FROM ABOVE   FROM BELOW

A left wing arose led by **Gerrard Winstanley**.

Winstanley said he spoke for the 'poor despised ones of the earth', the people whom even the Leveller movement did not represent. The Diggers, as Winstanley's followers came to be known, took direct action to put their ideas into practice.

15

In 1649 a group of them began to dig up the wasteland on St George's Hill, outside London. They wanted to farm it as a symbol of collective ownership. Local property owners were outraged that landless upstarts should be so bold, but the Diggers held firm to Winstanley's words: 'The poorest man has as true a title, as just a right, to land as a rich man.'

16

Soldiers were called in to break up their experiment. Dozens of similar initiatives in other areas were also suppressed. The Diggers were easily defeated because their leaders were pacifists.

The Diggers were idealists. They looked backwards to village communities as the basis of social organization.

COCKAYGNE

The struggle for freedom breaks out continually throughout class society. Even when people lack the organization to fight for it openly, they talk and sing about freedom. The dream of a better world always exists among common people. The ideal of a happy place, with no hierarchy, no sexual repression, no work and no worry constantly subverts the ruling class demand that the poor have to put up with their lot.

THIS TRAIN IS BOUND FOR FREEDOM!

HARRIET TUBMAN

SAM SHARPE*

THOMAS MUNTZER

In Britain in the middle ages the dream land was called **Cockaygne** (it was Cocquaine in France). It has other names too: Pomona, Venusberg, the City of Caesars, the Country of the Young and the Big Rock Candy Mountain.

*Jamaican leader of slave rebellion 1790

19

COCKAYGNE

There are birds in every bush,
Throstle, nightingale and thrush,
Woodpecker and the soaring lark,
More there are than man may mark,
Singing with all their merry might,
Never ceasing day or night.
Yet this wonder add to it—
That geese fly roasted on the spit,
As God's my witness, to that spot,
Crying out, 'Geese, all hot, all hot!'
Every goose in garlic drest,
Of all food the seemliest.
And all larks that are so couth
Fly right down into man's mouth,
Smothered in stew, and thereupon
Piles of powdered cinnamon:
Every man may drink his fill
And needn't sweat to pay the bill.

BIG ROCK CANDY MOUNTAIN

In the Big Rock Candy Mountains
All the cops have wooden legs,
All the bulldogs have rubber teeth,
And the hens lay soft boiled eggs.
The farmers' trees are full of fruit
And the barns are full of hay,
Oh I'm bound to go, where there ain't no snow,
Where the rain don't fall, where the wind don't blow.

The little streams of alcohol
Come a-trickling down the rocks...
There's a lake of stew and whisky too.

There ain't no short-handled shovels,
No axes, saws or picks'
I'm bound to stay where they sleep all day,
Where they hung the Turk that invented work,
In the Big Rock Candy Mountains.

20

POOR MAN'S HEAVEN

In Poor Man's Heaven we'll have our own way,
There's nothing up there but good luck,
There's strawberry pie
That's twenty feet high
And whipped cream they bring in a truck...
We'll eat all we please
Off ham and egg trees,
That grow by the lake full of beer.

UTOPIAS

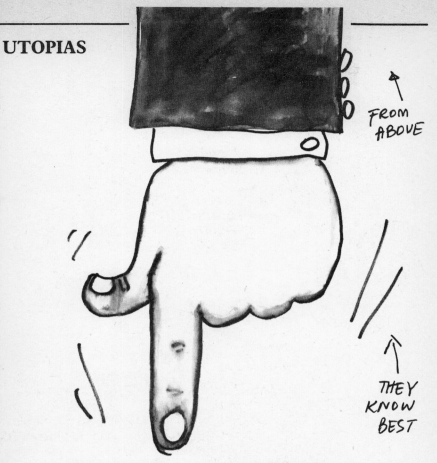

FROM ABOVE

THEY KNOW BEST

Whenever the oppressed rise up against inequality and injustice, the rich condemn them as a 'mob' and a 'rabble'. They put down rebellions with enormous cruelty but remained convinced of their own moral superiority.

There have always been those among the ruling class, however, who feel sorry for the poor and want to relieve their misery. These are the **Utopians**. They dream up ideal societies – Utopias – for the poor to live in, but which they don't want common people to organize for themselves. (It never occurs to them that ordinary folk might have that ability.) They invent schemes in which liberty, like charity, can be carefully doled out to the deserving poor.

WE GUARDIANS HAVE DEMOCRATICALLY DECIDED...

THAT THE **MOST EQUAL** GO IN A ROW ON THE LEFT, THE **NEXT** MOST EQUAL ON THE RIGHT AND THE **LEAST** EQUAL **UNDERNEATH**

Superficially, some early Greek societies appear socialist. The Spartan system, for example, which flourished until 146 BC, was based on the state ownership of land. Children were brought up collectively, people ate communally at public tables, and land was equally distributed. But it was not democratic.

It had two kings, and a class of semi-slaves – helots – to do all the work. Those who formed the collective government were an elite, whose sole ambition was to organise wars against neighbouring states.

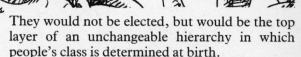

PLATO

Plato's famous *Republic* proposes a society run by Guardians, who make their decision communally.

They would not be elected, but would be the top layer of an unchangeable hierarchy in which people's class is determined at birth.

Plato was a conservative critic of Athenian democracy, which he took to mean the rule of the mob. He complained that there was too much liberty because craftsmen, peasants and shopkeepers could freely debate in the Assembly, vote and stand for election to public office. Radical critics wanted more, not less, democracy.

The *Republic* was a profoundly conservative ideal, but achieved an important, if undeserved, reputation. For centuries it was a major influence on democratic thinkers, who believed that legislation from above could bring equality. It was the inspiration for **Thomas More's** famous *Utopia*, published in Britain in 1516.

25

MORE'S UTOPIA

Utopia, which means both 'nowhere' and 'a beautiful place' in Greek, is More's imaginary island. Private property has been abolished. Everybody takes equal turns to work on the land.

OF COURSE THE **DIRTY** WORK IS DONE BY THOSE WHO ARE **LESS** EQUAL THAN THE OTHERS — ADULTERERS, RELIGIOUS ZEALOTS, P.O.W.s, THAT SORT OF THING — THEY'RE **BONDSMEN**

RELIGIOUS ZEALOTS, EH, THOMAS? OFF WITH THEIR HEADS, I SAY!

THOMAS MORE

KING HENRY VIII

There are many fine things about Utopia. Utopians live simply, but not poorly. They despise gold (they use it for chamber-pots), and believe in the pursuit of pleasure. Intellectual activities such as studying art and literature are highest rated, but 'eating, drinking, defaecating, scratching and copulating' are also to be enjoyed.

26

Prisoners of war (Utopians have an aggressive foreign policy, sending out their excess population to found colonies elsewhere), convicted criminals and religious zealots are the 'bondsmen' who do the dirty work so their betters can be equal.

Nevertheless, Utopia has been an important inspiration to socialists. Like Plato, More pleaded for a society based on reason. Like other Utopian idealists he condemned injustice and argued for an egalitarian and communally-run alternative. But like other Utopians, More provides no mechanism for achieving his ideal. Utopians do not understand that people can only win freedom for themselves...

After Plato and More's schemes there were many other Utopian plans. An amazing number were drawn up in France before and after the 1789 Revolution. The French Revolution, whose effects were felt all over the world, showed clearly how freedom means different things to people of different classes.

THE FRENCH REVOLUTION

The French Revolution of 1789 was a massive popular movement against the decaying feudal order. United round the slogan 'Liberty, Equality and Fraternity', Parisians overthrew the king, who was sent to the guillotine. France became a republic.

Robespierre and the **Jacobins** seized the leadership of the revolution. They represented the interests of the rising merchant (bourgeois) class. Everybody fought for liberty, but to the Jacobins liberty meant the right to run business and own property. To the Parisian poor (*Sansculottes*), such liberty meant little more than the 'freedom' to sell their labour to the rich.

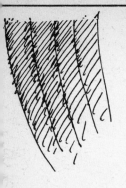

The different meaning of liberty to different classes led to a further split in the revolution. A radical wing developed in opposition to the Jacobins, known as *les Enragés*. Led by men like **Jacques Roux, Theophile Leclerc** and **Jean Varlet**, *les Enragés* argued that liberty for all meant more than mere constitutional rights.

Unfortunately, the radical idea of freedom argued for by *les Enragés* could not be achieved in France at the time. The economy was undeveloped and backward. Food was scarce. The standard of living was almost universally low. So long as there was not enough bread for everybody, ideas about freedom for all were doomed to remain as dreams in people's heads, or else destined to become isolated experiments. The material conditions for freedom from want did not exist.

THREE HOURS SPENT OUTSIDE A BAKERY WOULD DO MORE TO TRAIN A LEGISLATOR THAN ERR...

... FOUR YEARS ON THE BENCHES OF THE CONVENTION

THEO. LECLERC

REVOLUTION OUTSIDE FRANCE

The call to revolution was not confined to France. It was heard throughout the French colonies, and nowhere more powerfully than from the 'Black Jacobins' of San Domingo, France's most important colony in the Caribbean.

San Domingo was first colonized at the close of the middle ages, when Spain, France, Britain, Portugal and Holland raced to plunder the world.

The 'Indians' of San Domingo were enslaved and forced to work for their slavemasters. When they could stand no more they clubbed their children to death and committed mass suicide. Thousands of Africans were kidnapped and shipped across the Atlantic to replace the labour that had been 'lost' to the colonists. Slaves continually resisted their oppressors, but the revolts were usually isolated and put down brutally.

Toussaint
L'Ouverture

All this changed in 1789. While the revolutionaries in France took five years to declare an end to slavery, the Black Jacobins seized power for themselves. Led by **Pierre Toussaint L'Ouverture**, a superb politician and military tactician, their guerilla force overcame both the resistance of former owners and powerful armies sent by Spain and Britain.

32

When **Napoleon** came to power in 1799 he sent 30,000 of his most experienced troops to restore slavery. Toussaint was captured and taken to France, where he died in prison. The combination of a people's army and yellow fever, however, annihilated Napoleon's expeditionary forces. In 1804 San Domingo was declared an independent republic, to be called by its former Indian name, *Haiti* – the place of mountains.

Napoleon Bonaparte

Slaves in other colonies followed the Black Jacobins' lead. Slaves rebelled in British Guiana (Guyana) in 1808 and again in 1823, in Barbados in 1816, Jamaica in 1824 and 1831, and Antigua in 1831.

Rebellions in the Caribbean were followed by fights against slavery on the American mainland. The British slave trade was brought to an end in 1807, largely due to the self-organization of slaves, and slavery itself was officially abolished in the remaining British colonies in 1833. But in the Southern states of America slavery remained legal until 1863.

33

During the intervening years, thousands of slaves escaped from the South to freedom in the North. They were helped by white abolitionists (many of them Quakers) and by former slaves. An 'Underground Railway', in which women played a prominent part, provided safehouses and support for the runaways.

HARRIET TUBMAN

Harriet Tubman was one leading activist. Known as 'the Moses of her people', she led thousands of slaves to freedom on the Underground Railroad. She claimed that she never lost a 'passenger' and continued her work for many years, despite a $10,000 price on her head.

After the emancipation of the slaves, women like Harriet Tubman found themselves with yet another battle to face – this time for their rights as women. As her fellow-activist, **Sojourner Truth**, put it, equality for some cannot be won at the expense of others:

> *"There is a great stir about colored men getting their rights and not a word about colored women getting theirs. You see the colored man will be master over the woman and it will be just as bad as before. I have been forty years a slave and forty years free and would have forty years more to have equal rights for all."*

WHEN THE TRUE HISTORY OF THE ANTI-SLAVERY CAUSE SHALL BE WRITTEN, WOMAN WILL OCCUPY A LARGE SPACE IN ITS PAGES, FOR THE CAUSE OF THE SLAVE HAS BEEN PECULIARLY A WOMAN'S CAUSE

FREDERICK DOUGLASS, JOURNALIST, EX-SLAVE, LEADING ABOLITIONIST.

TOM PAINE

Another important spin-off from the French Revolution was the effect it had on the English-born radical, **Tom Paine**. In 1791 he published *The Rights of Man*, a defence of the Jacobin demands which condemned the arbitrary powers of the ruling classes everywhere in language that working people could understand.

FROM A SMALL SPARK KINDLED IN AMERICA, A FLAME HAS ARISEN, NOT TO BE EXTINGUISHED. WITHOUT CONSUMING, IT WINDS ITS PROGRESS FROM NATION TO NATION... ER, HAVE YOU INDIANS GOT A LIGHT?...

YOU'D THINK THEY OWNED THE PLACE

NEVER ASKED US TO THEIR TEA-PARTY!

Paine argued that people should be free to choose their own government. A democratically-elected government, he observed, could cut spending on the armed forces, do away with bureaucrats and sinecures, and provide social services and free education for all. His book became a textbook for the emerging working class movement. It was banned, but sold thousands of copies, was translated into many languages, and is still in print today.

... MAN FINDS HIMSELF **CHANGED**, AND DISCOVERS THAT THE STRENGTH AND POWERS OF DESPOTISM CONSIST **WHOLLY** IN THE **FEAR** OF RESISTING IT.

HE HATES THE RICH, YOU KNOW. LOATHES THEIR GUTS

THE SCALE OF THIS DRAWING'S A BIT ODD ISN'T IT?

Tom Paine originally made his name for his spirited defence of the American Revolution. His pamphlet, *Common Sense* (1776), vigorously supported independence. A committed republican, Paine was a fierce critic of the British monarchy and its supporters. He said that they could easily be removed if people would only realise their own strength.

Such criticism provoked a charge of seditious libel from the British authorities and Paine had to flee to France. His ideas, however, had taken firm root, thriving in the novel conditions of the Industrial Revolution.

THE INDUSTRIAL REVOLUTION

MY FAMILY FARMED THE SAME BIT OF LAND FOR GENERATIONS, UNTIL PARLIAMENT SNATCHED IT AWAY WITH THEIR 'ENCLOSURES ACT' IN 1760 AND GAVE IT TO THE GENTRY. NOW THERE'S NO LIVING FOR MY BROTHERS AND SISTERS EXCEPT IN THE MINES AND FACTORIES

The French Revolution gave birth to a radical idea of freedom: the notion that legal rights were not enough, that real freedom means freedom from want for everybody. The Industrial Revolution provided the wealth to make that dream a reality.

I KNOW WORKING FOR MASTER GEORGE IS BORING...

AND DANGEROUS, UNHEALTHY AND APPALLINGLY LOW PAID

The Industrial Revolution began in Britain in the last half of the eighteenth century. Between 1761 and 1844 the landed gentry used thousands of Enclosure Acts to expropriate over five and a half million acres of land. Villagers, deprived of their smallholdings and traditional commoners' rights, were transformed into landless labourers. In Scotland the process was so ruthless that whole regions were depopulated.

The poor were forced to move to the towns to sell their labour in the new factories that were springing up everywhere. Working conditions were harsh and unhealthy. Men, women and children alike toiled for up to 18 hours a day, seven days a week, for pitifully low wages.

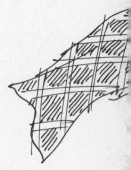

Ironically, while factory production meant immense suffering and hardship for workers, it was also in a way a step forward. The basis was being laid for developments which could liberate workers from exploitation and drudgery forever. The shift from small units to large-scale production not only required the close co-operation of great numbers of people, but also offered the possibility of producing such great surpluses that there would be an end to the tyranny of want.

The individual factory owners, of course, did not use the new technology for communal benefit. Rather than shorten working hours and enrich workers' lives, they increased exploitation to enhance their profits.

NED LUDD

THE LUDDITES

Not surprisingly, workers resented the introduction of new machines which deprived them of independent work and forced them to accept starvation wages and massive unemployment. In the late 18th century, and again between 1811 and 1816, thousands of workers rioted and broke up the new machines.

Machine-breakers in towns were known as **Luddites**, after those who smashed knitting frames in Nottinghamshire and signed their leaflets 'Ned Ludd', the legendary King Ludd of ancient Britain. In the countryside, farm workers rose up against threshing machines under the equally mythical **Captain Swing**. Some Luddites were also fired by the spirit of the French Revolution. In one leaflet they wrote:

> *"Come let us follow the brave example of the citizens of Paris who brought a tyrant to the ground."*

LIVE WORKING

There was a similar movement for the right to work in France. In 1830, striking silk workers in Lyon took over the town. The slogan on their banner read: 'Live working or die fighting'.

Such early risings were often led by skilled workers organised in the ancient craft unions or guilds which had existed from the middle ages. The new industrial workers had yet to form their own organizations.

EARLY RISINGS? YOUNG CHILDREN USED TO WORK 6 A.M. TILL 7 P.M. IN THE MILLS AND MINES

WHAT YOU MEAN, USED TO? IN SOME PLACES WE STILL ARE

THE FIRST SOCIALISTS

Early socialists were outraged by the contradiction between the possibilities offered by industrial production and the harsh realities of capitalist production. They argued that industry and agriculture should be organized along more socially responsible lines – which is how they got their name.

Socialists proposed that production should be run co-operatively and that workers should live communally. Hundreds of alternative socialist plans were drawn up in Britain and in France during the early 1800s. The details varied, but they all had one thing in common: they tried to help the suffering masses *from above*. None of them seriously entertained the idea of oppressed people fighting to free themselves. But in spite of their shortcomings, the ideas had great influence over later socialists.

French Utopian socialists were notable for their strong emphasis on sexual liberation and women's equality – elements largely ignored by many later socialisms.

SAINT-SIMON'S SOCIALISM

Henri, Comte de Saint-Simon, dreamed of a world without war, organised religion, or racial intolerance; a global social order in which science governs life and there is no social oppression. He promoted sexual freedom and the rights of women, and even designed clothes with the buttons at the back to encourage co-operation. It is little wonder that his vision has been called the 'Religion of the Engineers'.

The society he foresaw was efficient – but unequal and undemocratic. Rigidly organised, and highly centralised, all power was to be held by the 'Industrials' – not the working class but a managerial elite of bankers and technologists. Most of his detailed but absurd plans were never put into practice. We can still see his principles at work in the modern enthusiasm for the rule of 'experts'

LET'S **USE** THE POTENTIAL OF SCIENCE AND TECHNOLOGY — TAKE THE POWER FROM THE **IDLERS** AND GIVE IT TO THE **INDUSTRIALS**

YOU MEAN THE **WORKERS**?

NO, NO! BANKERS! **TECHNOCRATS!** SYSTEMS ANALYSTS! BUSINESS STUDIES LECTURERS!

←—ST. SIMON

'IF FRANCE HAD THE MISFORTUNE TO LOSE THE 10,000 RICHEST LANDOWNERS — IT WOULD RESULT IN NO POLITICAL LOSS FOR THE STATE'

who control property but do not own it. Nationalisation of industry in the West, the state-run economies of Eastern Europe and even the government-directed 'modernisation' programmes of Third World countries owe much to Saint-Simon's outlook. What they all have in common is the dream of social development without the need for a workers' movement.

45

FOURIER'S SOCIALISM

Charles Fourier wanted to establish a society of communes – 'phalansteries' (phalanx + monastery) – in which everyone is free to do what they want while at the same time working for the common good. He believed that work should be pleasurable, with people changing their jobs as often as they liked to prevent boredom. He thought children should be allowed to learn what

KIDS ENJOYING CLEANSING DEPT. DUTIES →

they are interested in, and not be forced into doing what adults think is good for them.

Fourier also believed in equal rights for women, and thought housework should be communally organized to liberate women. He spent a good deal of time drawing up blueprints for his myriad schemes, which he hawked around to wealthy philanthropists. Individual communities were established, chiefly in America, but none survived very long. In Britain his contemporary **Robert Owen**, developed similar ideas.

OWEN'S SOCIALISM

Robert Owen, a wealthy industrialist who had risen from poverty, became famous for his model factory at New Lanark in Scotland. He refused to employ young children, and provided an education for older ones. Hours of work were limited, decent housing was provided, and he established a co-operative store. In 1827, Owen coined the term 'socialism' to describe his experiment.

Convinced of the power of example to generate a 'revolution of the human mind' (the only kind he could tolerate), Owen set up further model communities in the south of England and at New Harmony, Indiana. They all failed.

On his return from America, Owen concentrated on developing the co-operative movement. But dissatisfaction with its limitations drew him to set up Britain's first country-wide union, the Grand National Consolidated Trades Union (1834).

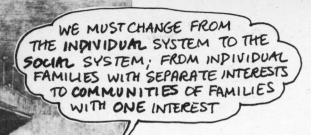

The Grand National Union grew at an amazing pace. In a few weeks over half a million workers had joined. In spite of Owen's plans to reconcile classes, employers were hostile to the Union. Within six months the Union was worn down by a series of strikes and lockouts. Owen summoned a congress. Overnight he turned the Union into 'The British and Foreign Consolidated Association of Industry, Humanity and Knowledge', whose aim was to realise his vision of a 'New Moral World' without competition. It failed.

All the communities founded by Utopian socialists failed. Their legacy, however, is still with us in the Garden Cities and New Towns of the post-war era, all built in a rural setting.

49

Not all Utopian socialists discounted the possibility of workers freeing themselves though. Two in particular deserve mention – **Gracchus Babeuf** and **Flora Tristan**.

Babeuf thought that only the common ownership of wealth – communism – could lay the basis for true freedom. His vision was of a society run communally by workers. But in the aftermath of the French Revolution he and his followers saw little possibility of winning a mass of workers to such an idea.

In desperation they looked for short cuts. Their solution was the Conspiracy of Equals, a plot to seize power and set up an Educational Dictatorship which would inform workers how good communism was. The Equals were arrested and Babeuf was sent to the guillotine in 1797.

STOLE IT?
I LIBERATED
IT FOR THE
CLASS

The subsequent history of France shows many such attempts at violent coups by dedicated bands of revolutionaries, all of which were brutally put down. Many were inspiring idealists, like **Auguste Blanqui**, who learnt his tactics from survivors of the Equals' conspiracy. They did not appreciate the need to root their organisations in the industrial proletariat.

In the 1840s, **Flora Tristan** was the first to argue for an international union of workers which could fight for workers' freedom. She coined the phrase 'Workers of the World Unite', which Karl Marx later stole.

Flora Tristan's ideal union was modelled on the medieval craft unions or guilds. She saw them as the base for organising 'Palaces of Labour', which would be the focus of all social and political activity. A strong feminist, she believed that women's

emancipation would only come with the ending of wage slavery.

Some points from Flora Tristan's Programme of Objectives:

- To constitute the working class by setting up a compact, solid, and indissoluble union.
- To proclaim the legitimacy of hands as property, 25 million French workers having no property other than their hands.
- To secure the recognition of every man and woman's right to work.
- To proclaim the urgent necessity of giving working class women moral, intellectual and vocational training so that they may improve the morals of men.
- To proclaim the fact that juridical equality between men and women is the only means of achieving the unity of humanity.

TRADES UNIONS

The birth of modern trades unions forced enormous changes in existing notions of socialism. They showed that workers, as a class, had independent interests.

For centuries, guilds for craft workers had regulated apprenticeships and wages. Industrial developments had greatly reduced their power, but employers feared them, and in Britain they were legally banned by the Combination Acts passed in 1799 and 1800. The laws were never wholly effective and they were repealed in 1824. From then on there was a huge upsurge in workers' organizations; new industrial workers began to form unions too.

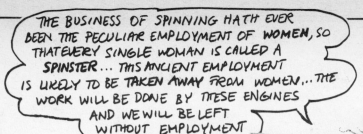

THE BUSINESS OF SPINNING HATH EVER BEEN THE PECULIAR EMPLOYMENT OF **WOMEN**, SO THAT EVERY SINGLE WOMAN IS CALLED A **SPINSTER** ... THIS ANCIENT EMPLOYMENT IS LIKELY TO BE TAKEN AWAY FROM WOMEN ... THE WORK WILL BE DONE BY THESE ENGINES AND WE WILL BE LEFT WITHOUT EMPLOYMENT

JOHN DOCHERTY'S ONLY A TEXTILE WORKER LIKE ME. WE SHOULD ALL UNIONIZE TOGETHER

Trades unions began with local attempts to organize workers in the same trade. But in 1829, after a disastrous six months' strike by Manchester spinners, the spinners' societies held a national conference. They realised that local organizations were not strong enough to take on the employers and they formed a national union – the Cotton Spinners Federation. The Federation had one sad failing that has weakened union organisation ever since. The conference resolved that, while it urged women to form their own unions and pledged every support for their efforts to gain 'men's rates', 'this union shall include only men spinners and piecers'.

From the very beginning, trades unions were split along sex lines. Women workers had to fight both the employers and male hostility. Later on they did form their own unions, among them Oldham's Lodge of Ancient Virgins.

Although weakened by the division between women and men, trades unions sprang up in every industry and began the battle for workers' rights. In 1830 **Tommy Hepburn** led the coal miners of Northumberland and Durham to form a union. In the same year **John Doherty** set up the Potters' Union. In 1832 a Builders' Union was established, another general union to unite all in the same workplace, regardless of craft specialism.

CHARTISM

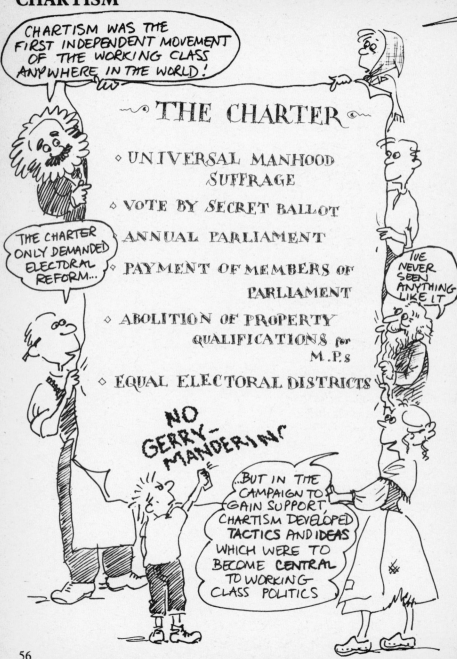

CHARTISM WAS THE FIRST INDEPENDENT MOVEMENT OF THE WORKING CLASS ANYWHERE IN THE WORLD!

THE CHARTER

◇ UNIVERSAL MANHOOD SUFFRAGE

◇ VOTE BY SECRET BALLOT

◇ ANNUAL PARLIAMENT

◇ PAYMENT OF MEMBERS OF PARLIAMENT

◇ ABOLITION OF PROPERTY QUALIFICATIONS for M.P.s

◇ EQUAL ELECTORAL DISTRICTS

THE CHARTER ONLY DEMANDED ELECTORAL REFORM...

I'VE NEVER SEEN ANYTHING LIKE IT

NO GERRY- MANDERING

...BUT IN THE CAMPAIGN TO GAIN SUPPORT, CHARTISM DEVELOPED TACTICS AND IDEAS WHICH WERE TO BECOME CENTRAL TO WORKING CLASS POLITICS

SONG OF THE LOWER CLASSES

We plough, we sow, we're so very, very low,
    That we delve in the dirty clay;
Till we bless the plain with the golden grain,
    And the vale with the fragrant hay.
Our place we know, we're so very, very low,
    'Tis down at the landlord's feet;
We're not too low the grain to sow,
    But too low the bread to eat.

> We're low, we're low – we're very, very low, –
>   And yet from our fingers glide
> The silken floss and the robes that glow
>   Round the limbs of the sons of pride;
> And what we get, and what we give,
>   We know, and we know our share;
> We're not too low the cloth to weave,
>   But too low the cloth to wear.

As well as work-based organizations, workers began to build their own political associations. Chartism was the first independent movement of the working class anywhere in the world. The People's Charter, drawn up in 1838, was a list of six demands for electoral reform whose aim was to achieve the vote for everybody, whether they owned property or not.

Its supporters, however, had aspirations far beyond the vote.

Like the trade unions, the Chartists refused to fight for women's rights. The demand for manhood suffrage was just what it said – votes for men, and men only. Women were active in the Chartist campaign, and even expected to get the vote, as a letter from a working woman to the Chartist paper, *The Northern Star*, declared:

> "It is the right of every working woman to
> have a vote in the legislation of her country."

But when **William Lovett** and other members of the Charter Committee met to draw up the Charter, demands for female suffrage were overruled on the grounds that 'its adoption in the Bill might retard the suffrage of men'.

Despite this, thousands of working women supported the campaign for the Charter. They demonstrated and rioted because they believed that the achievement of its demands would bring about further social changes.

> "We demand universal suffrage because it is
> our right; and not only because it is our right,
> but because it will bring freedom to our
> country, and happiness to our homesteads.
> We believe it will bring us bread and beef and
> beers."

The movement declined in the late 1840s, partly because of the extreme hostility of a ruling class faced with revolutions all over Europe. Yet Chartism had shown the enormous potential and organizational ability of the working class.

THE CHARTIST
MOVEMENT
DECLINED AFTER
1848 BUT MANY
OF ITS IDEAS
WERE CARRIED
OVER...

MARX AND ENGELS

The lesson was not lost on **Karl Marx** and **Frederick Engels**, two German socialists who came to live in England at the time. It became clear to them that socialism could not be won by appealing to people to be nice to each other, as Robert Owen had done. Instead, they declared that socialism would only be achieved from be-

low, by a struggle between classes, in which the working class organised itself to win a revolution.

Marx and Engels wrote prolifically about so many aspects of socialism that it is difficult to summarise their ideas. The most important thing to stress is that they made a complete break with the notion of socialism brought to the working class from above. They argued for the principles of workers' self-emancipation and workers' democracy.

64

Chartists had given birth to the concept that the working class could free itself through political struggle. Marx and Engels extended that to a principle – that only workers can free workers. Further, they firmly rejected the argument that capitalism could be reformed gradually from within. The conditions in which workers live force them to struggle against capitalist society at every turn, and it is this that makes the working class a revolutionary class.

Marx and Engels were the first leading socialists to support trade unions on principle. They completely rejected the idea that socialists could build socialist parties separate from the working class, and argued that socialists should fight for and develop socialist ideas within workers' organizations. All of this, and more, was forcefully proclaimed in their *Manifesto of the Communist Party*, published in 1848.

THE SHORTCOMINGS OF TRADE UNIONISM

THE COMMUNIST MANIFESTO & THE REVOLUTIONS OF 1848

The *Communist Manifesto* liberated socialism from conspirators and Utopians. In passionate yet rational language it declared that socialism could only be built by workers themselves. It was a watershed in socialist thought which is still relevant today, but its revolutionary spirit cannot be fully understood except against the backcloth of Europe at the time.

THE SPECTRE OF...

REFORMISM

ARISE YE STARVELINGS

COMMUNISTS ARE THE MOST ADVANCED SECTION OF WORKERS' PARTIES: THEY PUSH FORWARD ALL THE OTHERS. THEY UNDERSTAND THE AIMS, CONDITIONS & ULTIMATE RESULTS OF THE PROLETARIAN MOVEMENT, RON

DID YOU READ THAT IN THEIR 1848 MANIFESTO?

I NEVER HAVE ORIGINAL THOUGHTS

The Industrial Revolution, while advanced in Britain, was only just beginning in the rest of Europe. The working class was everywhere without political rights but commencing the battle to gain them. As the first line of the *Manifesto* declares, 'A spectre is haunting Europe, the spectre of Communism...'. Democratic revolution erupted.

In the year that the Chartists were presenting their final peaceful petition to the British Parliament, there were battles on the barricades in France. In February workers, students and the National Guard forced the 'citizen king', **Louis Philippe**, to abdicate and the Second Republic was declared. A socialist, **Louis Blanc**, became Labour Minister, proclaimed 'the right to work' and set up National Workshops for the unemployed.

A few weeks after the events in Paris, students in Vienna took to the streets with cries of 'Down with **Metternich**'. The old despot was forced to resign. Two days later, the Hungarian Diet set up a government largely independent of Austrian rule and freed serfs without compensation to landlords – demands soon taken up by the Czechs.

Upheavals in the Austrian empire in turn sparked countless revolts in Italy, which resulted in liberal constitutions and the establishment of a large number of city republics. Street fighting liberated Milan and Venice in March and, in November, the flight of the Pope inaugurated the Roman Republic.

There were also risings in Germany – in Baden Wurttemberg, in Bavaria and in Saxony. In Berlin the people demanded that Prussia should be granted a Constituent Assembly. There were movements to democratize the Swiss constitution. In Ireland, Denmark and Rumania nationalists revolted against foreign oppression.

They argued that a socialist party must involve large numbers of workers, and must be based on struggle. However, they also believed that this would naturally develop in a revolutionary direction, underestimating the possibility that people might fall for reformism – the idea of changing capitalism bit by bit.

● *young girl operating complex machinery in a South Carolina cottonmill, c. 1900*

73

MARX AND ENGELS ON WOMEN

Although Marx and Engels broke with the Utopians in every other way, they shared a passionate commitment to women's liberation. They, however, argued that women's position in society was ultimately determined by economic forces, and that women's liberation could only be won through a workers' revolution.

The commitment to women's equality was only one of the many issues that Marx and Engels fought for within the International Working Men's Association, of which they were founder members in 1864. This Association is now better known as...

THE FIRST INTERNATIONAL

The International was inspired by the militancy of workers in political movements all over Europe – particularly in the struggles for Polish independence and for Italian unification. Its delegates – from Britain, France, Poland, Italy and Switzerland – represented a wide spectrum of opinion, and its programme was broader and more moderate than that of the *Communist Manifesto*. Nevertheless it stated that working people must emancipate themselves, that their emancipation could only be achieved by a fight against class domination, and that the struggle was an international one.

The organization was supposed to bring about co-operation between trade union representatives and members of workers' parties, but its members were an ill-assorted lot who had deep differences on many issues. One of the major rifts was between anarchists and socialists. Both wanted a classless society, but anarchists were opposed to all authority, some seeing even workers' organizations themselves as a threat to personal liberty.

The two leading anarchists, **Pierre-Joseph Proudhon** and **Mikhail Bakunin**, had many fierce battles with Marx, and not surprisingly. Proudhon opposed capitalism but much else besides.

PROUDHON

Marx and Bakunin slogged out endless battles. Marx attacked Bakunin for his anti-party sentiments. Bakunin damned Marx as an authoritarian.

The constant faction fighting weakened the International immeasurably, and hostility to Marx's enthusiastic support for the Paris Commune finally killed it altogether.

THE PARIS COMMUNE

The Commune took place against a background of extreme demoralisation for the French government. The Prussians had just taken Paris after a four-month siege and **Napoleon III's** armies had been decimated. Sensing the government's weakness, workers went on the offensive. Frightened, the government fled to Versailles, the old royal palace. Soldiers were ordered to enter Paris in the early hours to take 400 cannon back to Versailles.

But milkmaids – who were already up and working before dawn – discovered what was happening and surrounded the soldiers. They raised the alarm, and the commanding Generals were summarily executed. By dawn workers had taken to the streets and within hours the city was theirs. The Commune was declared and the second siege of Paris started almost immediately.

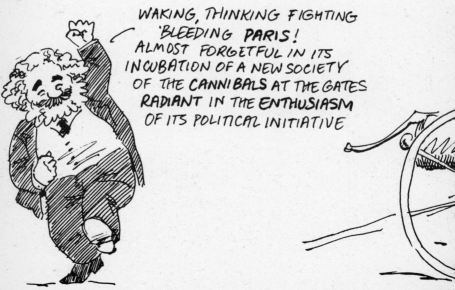

WAKING, THINKING FIGHTING 'BLEEDING PARIS! ALMOST FORGETFUL IN ITS INCUBATION OF A NEW SOCIETY OF THE CANNIBALS AT THE GATES RADIANT IN THE ENTHUSIASM OF ITS POLITICAL INITIATIVE

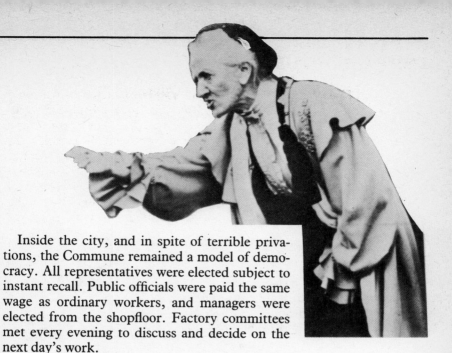

Inside the city, and in spite of terrible privations, the Commune remained a model of democracy. All representatives were elected subject to instant recall. Public officials were paid the same wage as ordinary workers, and managers were elected from the shopfloor. Factory committees met every evening to discuss and decide on the next day's work.

LES PETROLEUSES

HUH! I SHALL SAY NOTHING OF THEIR FEMALES OUT OF RESPECT FOR THE LADIES, WHOM THEY RESEMBLE ONLY WHEN THEY ARE DEAD!

The Commune was remarkable for the way women organized themselves. As individuals and as members of organizations like the *Union des Femmes* and the group of firebombers known as **Les Petroleuses** they fought alongside the men and organized the distribution of food. They demanded that all women – whether married or not – should have equal status. Despite this central role, women never got political rights within the Commune, and never gained the right to vote, but they supported the Commune to the end.

BUT THE COMMUNE WAS STILL A MODEL OF DEMOCRACY AND AN INSPIRATION TO US WHO BELIEVE IN WORKERS' SELF EMANCIPATION

The Communards survived two months of siege, bombardment and street-by-street fighting before being massacred. For every opponent of the Commune that died, twenty or more Communards were killed in the fighting or systematically shot in reprisal. Yet in spite of the defeat, the Commune showed both the real nature of class war and the revolutionary potential of workers.

Tried afterwards for her leading role in the Commune, **Louise Michel** declared in her speech from the dock:

LOUISE MICHEL

THE SOCIAL-DEMOCRATIC PARTIES:
THE PARLIAMENTARY ROAD TO SOCIALISM

From 1869, a new kind of socialist organisation sprang up all over Europe. These Social-Democratic parties had a mass membership among workers and stood for the 'socialisation of the means of production'; but while they included marxists among their members, their approach to socialism was often very different from that of Marx, or the French workers who fought for the Commune.

In Germany, the Social-Democratic leader **Ferdinand Lassalle** argued that the state – and not the working class – should be the means of introducing socialism. He led a movement which called itself socialist, but he also entered into secret negotiations with the German chancellor, **Bismarck**, urging him to set up a 'revolutionary people's monarchy'. Marx rightly accused Lassalle of behaving like a future workers' dictator.

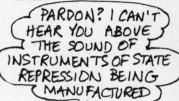

In spite of opposition from Marx, the German Marxist group joined up with Lassalle's organization. The Social-Democratic Party which resulted was enormously successful, swiftly becoming the largest party in Germany. In 1903 it had 81 members of Parliament. By 1912 it controlled nearly 100 newspapers, had about a million members and polled 5 million votes.

The size of the German party inspired many of its members to believe that it could act on behalf of the working class. The notion that class struggle was outdated was strengthened by the economic growth and prosperity of the time. Socialism, it seemed, would come about inevitably as soon as the workers' party became a majority in society.

The German Social-Democrat, **Eduard Bernstein** became the chief exponent of this evolutionary, 'peaceful road to socialism'. Leaders of other European socialist parties took a similar stance, which came to be called 'revisionism' because it 'revised away' Marx's revolutionary ideas.

In Britain the Fabians, founded in 1884, developed another evolutionary brand of socialism.

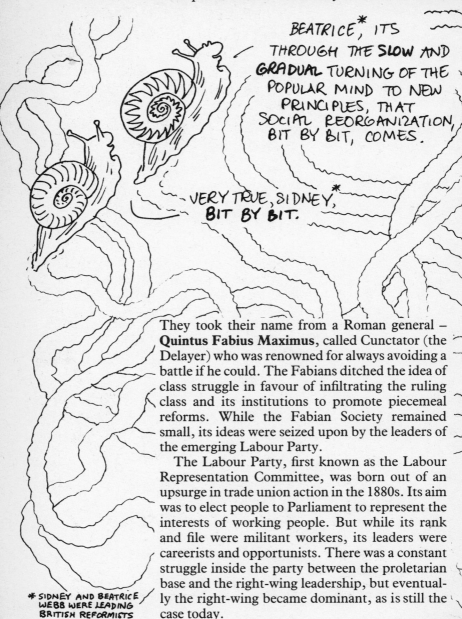

BEATRICE*, ITS THROUGH THE **SLOW** AND **GRADUAL** TURNING OF THE POPULAR MIND TO NEW PRINCIPLES, THAT SOCIAL REORGANIZATION, BIT BY BIT, COMES.

VERY TRUE, SIDNEY*, BIT BY BIT.

They took their name from a Roman general – **Quintus Fabius Maximus,** called Cunctator (the Delayer) who was renowned for always avoiding a battle if he could. The Fabians ditched the idea of class struggle in favour of infiltrating the ruling class and its institutions to promote piecemeal reforms. While the Fabian Society remained small, its ideas were seized upon by the leaders of the emerging Labour Party.

The Labour Party, first known as the Labour Representation Committee, was born out of an upsurge in trade union action in the 1880s. Its aim was to elect people to Parliament to represent the interests of working people. But while its rank and file were militant workers, its leaders were careerists and opportunists. There was a constant struggle inside the party between the proletarian base and the right-wing leadership, but eventually the right-wing became dominant, as is still the case today.

* SIDNEY AND BEATRICE WEBB WERE LEADING BRITISH REFORMISTS

ITS ALWAYS TOO EARLY FOR THE S.D.P.

ROSA LUXEMBURG

In Germany, too, there was a similar struggle. **Rosa Luxemburg,** a Polish socialist who had been forced to flee to Germany because of her political activity in Poland and Russia, argued vehemently against Bernstein's ideas. She asserted that the fight against exploitation and oppression could only be led by those who suffered from them. Further, she predicted that economic expansion could not continue forever: it would inevitably give way to economic depression and hence to war among the imperialist nations over control of the world's resources and markets. She was soon shown to be correct.

BOSSES AND WORKERS HAVE OPPOSING INTERESTS!

ONLY THE EXPLOITED CAN FIGHT THEIR OWN OPPRESSION

ROSA LUXEMBURG, A POLISH SOCIALIST ACTIVE AMONG THE GERMAN WORKERS.

SOCIALISM AND THE SECOND INTERNATIONAL

1889 - 2ND INTERNATIONAL FOUNDED. PRACTICALLY ALL THE SOCIALIST PARTIES IN THE WORLD JOIN.

REVOLUTIONARIES AND REFORMISTS IN THE INTERNATIONAL ARE RARELY IN AGREEMENT.

The First World war took most socialists by surprise. All the socialist parties in Europe were members of the Second International, founded in 1889, whose declared policy was opposition to war. In 1912 the International even resolved to organize an international rising of workers if capitalist governments went to war.

When war did break out the resolutions suddenly meant nothing. Many socialist leaders turned their back on the idea of a working class alliance against war and became active supporters of their own national mobilisations. It was the end of the Second International as a revolutionary organization.

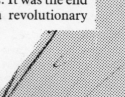

1912 – WAR DENOUNCED – INTERNATIONAL RISING OF WORKERS THREATENED IF CAPITALIST COUNTRIES GO TO WAR.

1914 – MOST SOCIALIST PARTY LEADERS **ABANDON** INTER-NATIONALISM, AND ESPOUSE **PATRIOTISM & THE WAR EFFORT.**

A minority of socialists in each national party continued their opposition to the war. In Britain **Sylvia Pankhurst**, a suffragette and a militant socialist, was a leading campaigner. In Germany, **Rosa Luxemburg, Clara Zetkin** and **Karl Liebknecht** led an opposition movement that was later to become the German Communist Party (1918). In their view, war was inherent in capitalism and only a working class revolution could end war forever.

In some countries militant workers proved sufficiently strong to stage insurrections. In 1919 there were uprisings in Germany, Hungary, Austria and Italy. But they were all defeated. Rosa Luxemburg and Karl Liebknecht were brutally murdered.

THE RUSSIAN REVOLUTION

In Russia, things went differently. Workers staged a successful revolution, led by a workers' party – the Bolsheviks.

RUSSIAN

The Bolshevik Party, whose best-known leader was **Lenin,** was very different from the nationalistic and reformist parties of Western Europe. But it also rejected the Russian revolutionary tradition of terrorism, on the grounds that it substituted the actions of dedicated politicos (terrorists) for workers' self-emancipation.

REVOLUTION

The Russian state, however, ruled by the Czar, was brutally repressive and totally banned the mass-party activity that was possible in Western Europe. In consequence the Bolsheviks organized a secretive, highly-disciplined and centralised party of committed revolutionaries which could win the leadership of workers' movements wherever they sprang up.

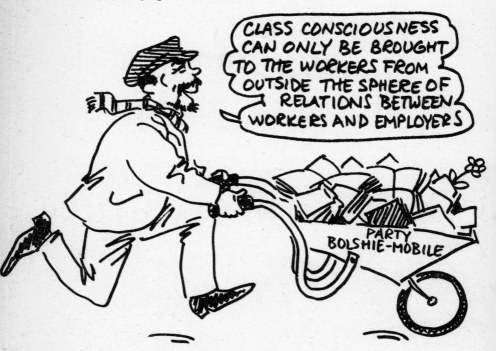

Lenin argued that workers should not just be concerned with economic, trade union issues; they also had to fight for state power. Early on, in his pamphlet *What Is to Be Done* (1902), he went so far as to say that: 'Class consciousness can be brought to workers only from outside the economic struggle' – an elitist argument for revolutionaries to take politics to the workers. Later, however, he changed his mind about this. The workers themselves, he noted, are never satisfied with 'peaceful economism'.

BUT LENIN WAS LATER TO CHANGE HIS MIND ABOUT THE USEFULNESS OF SPONTANEOUS ACTIONS BY WORKERS...

He also re-thought the way socialism would be achieved in Russia. Until 1917, Lenin believed that the working class and peasantry would first have to win the democratic revolution against Czarism in order to secure capitalism in Russia. In his view the middle class, which elsewhere in Europe had led bourgeois revolutions, had in Russia already ceased to be a radical force and was now incapable of leading a democratic revolution. This was very much in line with the currently orthodox Marxist assumption that no social revolution could skip a 'stage' of social development. Socialism would have to wait.

Leon Trotsky disagreed. Workers, he argued, were the only class that could lead the democratic revolution in a backward country; and the process did not have to stop there. The struggle for democratic rights would inevitably carry over into a struggle for workers' control and socialism. With the support of revolutions in advanced countries, Russia could miss out a stage and move straight to its own revolution. Trotsky's theory was called *Permanent Revolution*, perhaps more accurately described as 'the continuous revolution'.

95

GIVE US BREAD!

WE WANT HERRINGS!

WAIT! NOT UNTIL THE PARTY SAYS SO!

INTERNATIONAL WOMENS DAY

COMRADE KAYUROV (A BOLSHEVIK)

OCTOBER 1917

In the words of one observer:

"The Russian Revolution was begun by hungry women demanding bread and herrings. They started by wrecking the tramcars and looting a few small shops. Only later did they, together with workers and politicians, become ambitious to wreck the Russian autocracy."

When women textile workers took to the streets of Petrograd in February 1917, few people thought that it would start a revolution. The Bolshevik Party had categorically forbidden its member's to take part, saying that workers were not yet strong enough to take on the police and troops. Once the demonstrations started, however, they spread and grew into a massive workers' movement. Bolsheviks and all other left parties joined in.

Within weeks the Czar was overthrown and a Provisional Government established which promised many reforms. Lenin, who was exiled in

Switzerland at the time, saw what was happening and acknowledged that Trotsky's ideas about Permanent Revolution were correct. He returned to Russia at once and began the fight to convince the Bolsheviks to continue the struggle for workers' power. There was to be no halting at the level of the parliamentary republic.

For his part, Trotsky saw that a strong leadership was necessary to ensure the workers' revolution was successful. He joined the Bolsheviks and worked to recruit the workers' leaders to the Bolshevik Party.

The rising in the towns was supported by a massive revolt of peasants, who united round the Bolshevik slogan 'Bread, Peace and Land'.

The Bolshevik Party grew astronomically (from 24,000 to 240,000 between February and July). Its influence was felt in all popular committees, but particularly in the Soviets – the councils of workers' deputies.

OCTOBER 1917

Workers' Councils were first elected at workplaces and neighbourhoods in February 1917. They were democratic committees to decide all questions of production and distribution. Delegates were subject to recall – very much like the workers' committees of the Paris Commune.

Soviets became the political centre of the workers' movement. The Bolshevik Party rapidly gained a majority in them, and in October led the Revolution to kick out the Provisional Government. In its place, local workers' councils sent delegates to the 'All Russian Congress of Soviets', where national decisions were made.

THE FIRST RED FLAG AT THE FRONT

Immense social reforms were introduced liberalising abortion and marriage, making

TO THE

VIETS

divorce easy, providing free education for all and setting up the
first-ever welfare services. But for socialism to grow, mass
participation and legal reforms were not enough; peace and
economic growth were also necessary.

Until 1921 the country was riven by civil war, which saw anti-revolutionary forces ('Whites') aided and even joined by armies from Britain, USA, France, Czechoslovakia and Poland. A blockade cut Russia off from the rest of the world. Without access to foreign resources or markets, factories were forced to close down. Starvation was universal, and half the urban population had to return to the countryside.

Isolated and undermined, the revolution could not survive without international support, yet the workers' uprisings of 1919 in Germany, Hungary and elsewhere were defeated.

The Bolsheviks continued to rule Russia, but on behalf of a class that hardly existed as a coherent force any longer. The attempt to hang on to centralised control of the state even led to brutal suppression of workers' protests at home. The most infamous was the revolt led by starving sailors at the naval fortress of Kronstadt in 1921. Troops led by Trotsky crushed the rebellion.

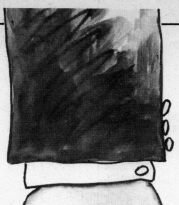

THE GLORIOUS
DICTATORSHIP
OF THE
PROLETARIAT!

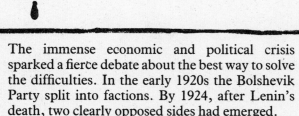

STALINISM

The immense economic and political crisis
sparked a fierce debate about the best way to solve
the difficulties. In the early 1920s the Bolshevik
Party split into factions. By 1924, after Lenin's
death, two clearly opposed sides had emerged.

One side, led by **Joseph Stalin**, wanted the
state to run industry and agriculture like one big
business. They backed Stalin's idea of 'Socialism
in One Country' in which a centralised, state-
controlled economy would be made strong
enough to compete with other industrialised
countries. The plan to force a gigantic increase in
industrial production from above inevitably
meant ditching workers' democracy.

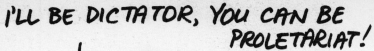

I'LL BE DICTATOR, YOU CAN BE PROLETARIAT!

The Left Opposition on the other hand, which included Trotsky, believed that democracy was essential to socialism. They argued that the problem could not be solved inside Russia alone, and said that Russia should encourage workers' revolutions elsewhere rather than try to compete with capitalist countries in industrial and military production.

Stalin fought ruthlessly for his ideas, not hesitating to murder those who opposed him. In 1927 he won. Trotsky was expelled from the Bolshevik Party and forced into exile. Stalin took over.

THE PURGES

Thousands of Party members were expelled in 1927 when Stalin organized to eliminate all opposition. In the 1930s there were 'show trials' at which leading Bolsheviks were forced to 'confess' to crimes publicly, then sentenced to death.

Less prominent party officials were subjected to the horror of slave camps in Siberia. According to some estimates, there were two million people in the camps in 1931. By 1933 there were five million. In 1942 the number had reached 15 million.

Strikes were outlawed in 1938. Trade unions became the voice of the management on the shop-floor. Parents were made legally accountable for the behaviour of their children. Abortion was made illegal. Homosexuality was outlawed. Sexual relations outside of marriage were described as 'promiscuity' and denounced for reducing the energy that workers had available for industrial production.

TODAY, RUSSIA AND ITS SATELLITES ARE STILL RUN ON THE PRINCIPLE OF GIVING THE WORKERS WHAT'S GOOD FOR THEM AND NOT ON SELF ORGANIZATION FROM BELOW.

I'M A BUREAUCRAT & I'M O.K.

MANY BELIEVE THAT STATE CONTROL IS THE ONLY ROAD TO EQUALITY AND FREEDOM

The terror continued until Stalin died in 1953. After that there were hopes for change. At the Twentieth Party Congress in 1956, Stalin's successor, **Nikita Krushchev,** denounced Stalin's cruelty and terrorism in a 'secret speech' which lasted six hours and spread over two days. But he did not repudiate Stalin's idea that socialism is something that the state does to workers for their own good. In spite of some 'liberalisation', control of Russian society still remains firmly in the hands of the people at the top of the party apparatus.

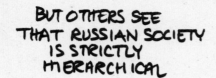

BUT OTHERS SEE THAT RUSSIAN SOCIETY IS STRICTLY HIERARCHICAL

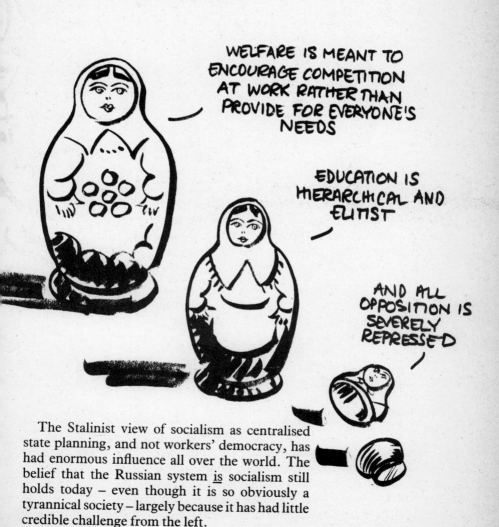

WELFARE IS MEANT TO ENCOURAGE COMPETITION AT WORK RATHER THAN PROVIDE FOR EVERYONE'S NEEDS

EDUCATION IS HIERARCHICAL AND ELITIST

AND ALL OPPOSITION IS SEVERELY REPRESSED

The Stalinist view of socialism as centralised state planning, and not workers' democracy, has had enormous influence all over the world. The belief that the Russian system _is_ socialism still holds today – even though it is so obviously a tyrannical society – largely because it has had little credible challenge from the left.

ANTI-STALINISM

Leon Trotsky represents an important attempt to challenge the equation of socialism with Stalinism. After Trotsky was expelled from Russia in 1927, he spent the rest of his life trying to keep alive the notion that socialism is workers' power, that it requires a democratic workers' party, and that it is internationalist.

Although Trotsky's followers are now few in number, his ideas are still important. When he won Lenin to his notion of Permanent Revolution in 1917, it undoubtedly changed the course of world history. Regrettably he failed to build up an effective opposition to Stalin inside Russia until it was too late.

Outside Russia, Stalin's propaganda left Trotsky isolated. Yet all through the 1930s he kept alive the idea of 'socialism from below', and wrote effectively on the defeat and demoralisation that had overtaken workers' movements. His pamphlets about how Stalinism allowed **Hitler** to rise to power in Germany and weakened the fight against fascism in Spain provided a reasoned socialist view which rekindled the will to struggle among many socialists.

In the late 1930s Trotsky's followers temporarily played a leading role in working class organization in America. But most of his organizational effort was less successful.

The events leading up to the Second World War led Trotsky to believe that the final crisis of capitalism was imminent. He thought that a mass movement of workers was about to be born, and called for the founding of a new – Fourth – International to replace the Stalinist Comintern.

But Trotsky was mistaken. The post-war period saw a massive economic boom whilst workers' organizations remained dormant and inactive. The Fourth International was a flop – tiny, and rent by interfaction rivalry.

TROTSKY IN EXILE...

Even the remotest possibility of a revival of ideas about 'socialism from below' was too much for Stalin. He sent agents to Mexico, where Trotsky was living. In 1940, a Stalinist assassin murdered him with an ice-pick as he sat working.

STALINISM INTERNATIONAL LTD.

Stalin's success in eliminating opposition both inside and outside Russia meant that his definition of socialism went unchallenged. Once established, the theory of 'socialism in one country' had a devastating effect on the workers' movement internationally. If socialism could be established in Russia alone, there was no need for Russia to encourage revolutionary movements elsewhere.

COMMUNISTS ELSEWHERE CAN POSTPONE MAKING REVOLUTIONS TILL LATER...

WE MUST SPEND OUR TIME DENYING SLANDERS ABOUT SLAVE CAMPS.

IMPERIAL-IST LIES!

AND GAINING INFLUENCE IN PARLIAMENT

Indeed, to do so would damage Russia's attempts to become a respectable trading nation. Instead of supporting workers' struggles then, Russia's resources were directed away from class struggle and towards coexistence with capitalist regimes.

COMMUNIST HAIRDRESSING EXHIBITION

Young Communist   Party Man   Shock Worker   Nervous Breakdown.

115

CHINA 1927

When Chinese workers rose in Shanghai in 1927, the Chinese Communist Party was a leading force among them. But instead of trying to spread their revolution to other cities, Chinese communists were instructed by Stalin to do nothing that might threaten their alliance with the nationalist Kuomintang. The Kuomintang, in a classic counter-revolution, soon sought the assistance of British, US, Japanese and French militias, and slaughtered the communists. Stalin defended his policy by saying that the Chinese proletariat was as yet too weak to survive without 'their' bourgeoisie.

It was as if 1917 had never happened.

SPAIN 1936

Another tragedy was the Spanish Civil War. Elections in 1936 had returned a Popular Front Government of liberal republicans, socialists and communists. Extreme right groups and the army, led by **General Franco**, promptly rose in rebellion. They met massive popular resistance.

Thousands of socialists from all over the world joined the International Brigades and went to Spain to join the fight against fascism and to defend the new society being built by the republicans. One of them, the writer **George Orwell**, described the atmosphere:

While fascist governments in Germany and Italy were sending guns, planes and 40,000 'volunteers' to Franco, Britain and France – which also had a Popular Front government – signed a non-intervention treaty. Stalin, too, refused material help. Instead of sending arms to the republicans, he ordered the Spanish Communists to treat others on the left the same way he was already dealing with them in Russia. Anarchists (who through the CNT – the National Confederation of Labour – organized two million workers) and Trotskyists were denounced as counter-revolutionaries.

IT WAS THE FIRST TIME I HAD EVER BEEN IN A TOWN WHERE THE **WORKING CLASS** WAS IN THE SADDLE. PRACTICALLY EVERY BUILDING OF ANY SIZE WAS DRAPED WITH **RED FLAGS** ... ALMOST EVERY CHURCH WAS GUTTED AND ITS IMAGES BURNT ... EVERY SHOP HAD BEEN **COLLECTIVIZED** ... WAITERS AND SHOP WORKERS LOOKED YOU IN THE FACE AND TREATED YOU AS AN **EQUAL** ... THIS REALLY WAS A WORKERS' STATE ... ABOVE ALL THERE WAS A BELIEF IN **REVOLUTION** AND THE **FUTURE**, A FEELING OF HAVING EMERGED INTO AN ERA OF **EQUALITY** AND **FREEDOM**. HUMAN BEINGS WERE TRYING TO BEHAVE AS **HUMAN BEINGS** AND NOT AS COGS IN A CAPITALIST MACHINE.

GEORGE ORWELL

The Russian newspaper, *Pravda*, soon noted with satisfaction that: 'The cleaning up of Trotskyist and anarcho-syndicalist elements has already begun with the same degree of energy as in the USSR.'

ANARCHIST AND TROTSKYIST ELEMENTS ARE **COUNTER-REVOLUTIONARY FASCISTS** AND MUST BE AS ENERGETICALLY CLEANED UP AS THEY ARE IN THE U.S.S.R!

The infighting on the left led to the imprisonment and death of socialists, which vastly weakened the workers' movement. By 1939 Franco had won the war. A fascist party took control of Spain.

119

The instruction to communists to attack all other factions on the left as 'counter-revolutionary' or 'social fascists' also crippled the fight against fascism in pre-war Germany. Instead of uniting the left against the threat of **Hitler,** the German communists isolated themselves in 'red' unions, refused to work with others on the left, and split the leadership of the workers' movement. The Social Democrats were seen as a greater enemy than the Nazis. A strong and well-organised workers' movement was thus defeated and Hitler came to power.

YALTA 1945

After World War II, the Stalinist system was extended beyond Russia to most of the countries of Eastern Europe. Almost overnight, countries like Poland, Czechoslovakia and Hungary became 'socialist'. But the socialism wasn't the result of a workers' movement fighting to replace the old regimes with a workers' government. Quite the opposite. Their 'socialism' was imposed from above at the Yalta conference in 1945. Stalin, **Churchill** and **Roosevelt** carved up the world between them, awarding Russia a 'sphere of influence' in the east in return for a free hand for capitalism in the Mediterranean and Western Europe.

HUNGARY?

WANT ANY BRUSSELS?

DON'T YOU GO SLAVERING LIKE THAT

RUSSIA'S SATELLITES

Russia used its influence ruthlessly. Industrialisation was forced through regardless of human cost. Meanwhile, Russia plundered the natural resources of its new colonies. The Poles 'agreed' to sell 65 million tons of coal at such a price that Russia made 900 million dollars out of the deal. Yugoslavia was paid 45,000 dinars a ton for molybdenum sold to Russia. It cost 500,000 dinars a ton to produce.

Hungarian uprising 1956

LET'S TAKE CONTROL OF THE FACTORIES!

Despite industrialisation, standards of living fell; resources were directed away from production for need toward production for competition on the world market. Murder, torture, imprisonment and labour camps were used to intimidate all those who dared protest. In 1953 building workers in East Berlin rose up against the tyranny.

They were followed by Hungarian workers in 1956, Czech workers in 1968 and Polish workers in 1971, 1976 and 1980. Their rebellions were all crushed, but their actions exposed the lie that socialism exists in Eastern Europe. In 1980 Polish miners wrote in a Silesian miners' bulletin:

"Our system has nothing to do with Socialism: it is state capitalism in which there is no concern for workers' well-being. Miners are not important; the only thing that counts is the coal that can be exchanged for dollars."

Although workers in Eastern Europe were defeated, they showed how the system can be fought. The struggle of Polish workers continues, symbolised by their slogan: 'The winter is yours, but the spring will be ours.'

IMPERIALISM

The relationship between Russia and its satellites in Eastern Europe parallels the imperialism of western nations in the Third World.

NOW THAT CAPITALISM IS BEGINNING TO TAKE EFFECT...

AND THINGS ARE CALM AT HOME...

...LET'S SEE WHAT WE CAN GRAB OVERSEAS: GOLD! SILKS! SPICES! GOLD! COFFEE! JEWELS! SLAVES! GOLD!

(17th EMPIRE BUILDERS

From the very beginning of capitalism individual states tried to extend their economic power to the rest of the world. They built up vast empires through invasions, wars and the repression of native populations. Wealth was looted from the colonies, which were also used as sources of cheap raw materials and to provide labour and guaranteed markets.

Initially, gold was sought. All over the Caribbean native populations were exterminated by colonisers seeking precious metals. When later rulers wanted to use the islands to grow cash crops such as sugar, they had to import slave labour to replace the populations which had been butchered. More than 15 million slaves were shipped across the Atlantic from Africa. Another nine million died on the slave ships.

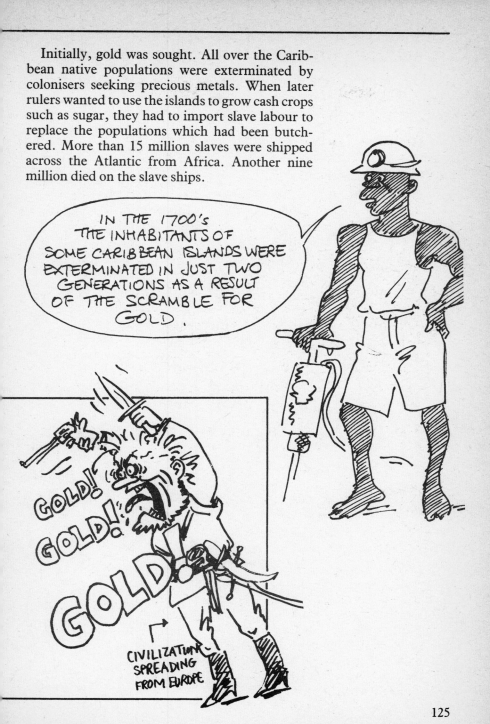

IN THE 1700's THE INHABITANTS OF SOME CARIBBEAN ISLANDS WERE EXTERMINATED IN JUST TWO GENERATIONS AS A RESULT OF THE SCRAMBLE FOR GOLD.

GOLD! GOLD! GOLD!

CIVILIZATION SPREADING FROM EUROPE

SLAVERY AND RACISM

ABOUT HALF THE SLAVE SHIPS WERE BRITISH. THE WEALTH GAINED FROM THE SLAVE TRADE HELPED TO FINANCE BRITISH INDUSTRY, WHICH IS WHY BRITAIN WAS ONE OF THE FIRST COUNTRIES TO BECOME INDUSTRIALISED.

AT ITS **PEAK** THE BRITISH EMPIRE WAS THE LARGEST EVER SEEN — COMPRISING A QUARTER OF THE WORLD'S POPULATION.

"THE VEILED SLAVERY OF THE WAGE WORKER IN EUROPE REQUIRED FOR ITS PEDESTAL SLAVERY PURE & SIMPLE IN THE NEW WORLD" MARX.

Slave labour in the colonies laid the basis for wage slavery in Britain. Eventually slavery was abolished. But even after slaves were freed, black people still suffered the racism that went hand in hand with slavery.

Imperialism reversed economic relationships across the world. During the seventeenth century, the wealth of India and China was greater than that of Europe. Their prosperity diminished as Europe grew rich.

Today direct imperialist looting of resources has been replaced by other kinds of domination. Western countries remain wealthy relative to the rest of the world because their superior productive forces are maintained by the West's control of technology, commodity markets and finance capital.

In some cases western governments deliberately prevent development elsewhere for the sake of their own manufacturing sector (the Indian cotton textile industry was destroyed in the

nineteenth century in order that Lancashire's cotton might thrive). But there are even more formidable obstacles to industrialisation in the Third World. Although ex-colonies are now formally independent they are tied by loans and debts to the West, and the cosmetic of economic 'aid' does nothing to redress the balance.

Industry has not confined itself to the West. Multinational companies have expanded to many parts of the world, for example, to South Korea, Taiwan, Hong Kong, and Singapore. Formerly populated by peasants, these countries now have sizeable working classes. Yet the shift of industry has made little difference to the gap between rich and poor nations. Relative poverty is locked into the system. The World Bank estimates that the poor countries, at current growth rates, will take 746 years to catch up with the present income per head of the rich countries. But if the rich countries continue to advance, the poor will never catch up.

NATIONAL LIBERATION

"Our revolution is neither capitalist nor communist. Capitalism sacrifices the human being, communism with its totalitarian concepts sacrifices human rights. We agree with neither one nor the other."
Fidel Castro 1959

The devastating effects of imperialism united the populations of colonial countries against 'white' rule. All classes were brutally oppressed by racism. Workers and peasants were terrorised into working for foreign businesses. The middle classes were slightly better off but still denied their political rights. They all came together in national liberation movements.

The fight for liberation from white rule inevitably affected ideas about freedom and socialism. Many black people rejected everything 'white', dismissed western socialism and instead tried to find their own way to equality through black movements and national liberation fronts.

Leaders of national liberation movements argued for political and economic independence. They promised land reforms and higher wages to peasants and workers. Idealistic students, workers, peasants and the middle classes came together under the same banner. The unity was powerful and expelled colonialists from countries all over Africa, Asia and most of Latin America.

Independence brought new problems, however. It secured political rights and allowed the black middle class to develop their business interests, but workers and peasants found that the higher wages and better living standards that they'd fought for simply did not materialise. Political independence did not bring economic independence. The newly 'independent' states were, as before, locked into a subordinate position in the world economy.

Although many of the leaders of national liberation movements were socialists, they soon found that socialism could not be built in one country alone against the pressures of the world economy. One by one the newly independent countries tried to introduce extensive nationalisation, a high pace of industrialisation and massive agrarian reform as a basis for socialism. But they found themselves as hamstrung as Russia had been in the 1920s. To survive they were forced to compete with other economies on the world market.

Workers were told they would have to work harder but wait until their economy 'caught up' with other countries before they could enjoy better living standards. But imperialism means that poor countries never catch up, and to obtain higher wages workers inevitably found themselves driven to strike against the very leaders they had supported in national liberation movements.

Coming home—South Africa

135

TANZANIA

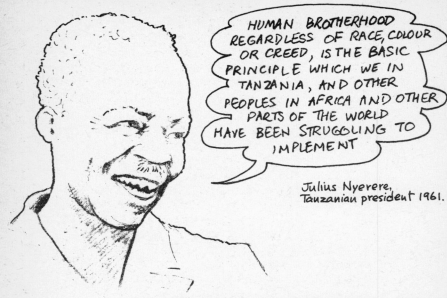

HUMAN BROTHERHOOD REGARDLESS OF RACE, COLOUR OR CREED, IS THE BASIC PRINCIPLE WHICH WE IN TANZANIA, AND OTHER PEOPLES IN AFRICA AND OTHER PARTS OF THE WORLD HAVE BEEN STRUGGLING TO IMPLEMENT

Julius Nyerere, Tanzanian president 1961.

In Tanzania, new agricultural co-operatives enthusiastically set about producing cash crops such as cashew nuts, tea and tobacco to pay for the import of western machinery for industry. This meant that food production for the home market was neglected. Workers were asked to produce more but there was less to eat. 60,000 workers responded with recurring strikes against Nyerere's 'socialism'.

ZIMBABWE

BLACK MAJORITY RULE?! **NO! NEVER IN A THOUSAND YEARS!**

IAN SMITH

IN '75, THE WHITE RHODESIAN GOVERNMENT MADE A UNILATERAL DECLARATION OF INDEPENDENCE FROM BRITAIN

ROBERT MUGABE

HULLO, SMITH? THIS IS THE PRIME MINISTER OF BRITAIN AND I'D JUST LIKE TO TELL YOU...

...HOW OUTRAGED I AM AT YOUR U.D.I. I MAY HAVE TO MAKE SOME NOISES ABOUT A TRADE EMBARGO. HOW'S THE WEATHER OVER THERE, OLD CHAP?

HAROLD WILSON (THE ONE ON THE COUCH)

BACKED BY STRIKES, ZANU AND ZAPU's* MILITARY VICTORY FORCED SMITH AND THE WHITE GOVERNMENT TO HOLD FREE ELECTIONS WHICH MUGABE OF ZANU EASILY WON!

*THE TWO NATIONALIST PARTIES

A black nationalist power structure has not brought economic freedom to the workers of Zimbabwe. It proved impossible to implement nationalisation, and concessions were made to white businesses and landowners in an effort to stabilise the economy so it could survive in the face of capitalist hostility. The marxist rhetoric of **Robert Mugabe** now goes hand in hand with the effort to make Zimbabwe competitive on the world market. The prime minister is black, but the economy is still controlled by decisions made in the boardrooms and commodity markets of New York and London.

AN OCCLUDED FRONT IS BRINGING RAIN FROM RACIST SOUTH AFRICA...

EMPTY MARXIST RHETORIC

YES, I VOTED FOR MUGABE! BUT BLACK AS HE IS, HE COULDN'T SWEEP AWAY THE DECISIONS OF THE INTERNATIONAL FINANCE HOUSES AND COMMODITY MARKETS WHICH CONTROL OUR COUNTRY'S ECONOMY.

139

ZAMBIA

Similarly in Zambia. Miners struck in support of **Kenneth Kaunda** during the pre-independence elections in 1964. Yet in 1966 the same miners led a strike demanding better wages and conditions. Kaunda conceded some wage rises, and allowed peasants to take over farms abandoned by white settlers. But in 1967 he outlawed strikes on the grounds that workers were too vital to the national economy to be allowed the freedom to strike.

BUT WE HERE OUT AGAIN IN '81!

So far no country has managed to break free of capitalism. The Cuban revolution of 1959 aspired to such freedom. After the corrupt **Batista** regime was overthrown, American capitalists were expelled and industry was nationalised. But economic boycotts forced Cuba into dependence on Russian controlled markets. Many gains have been made but the tyranny of American domination has been replaced by Russian influence.

140

INDIA

Even the Indian nationalist movement, the largest ever against imperialism, failed to achieve free-

dom and equality through economic growth. Led by **Mahatma Gandhi**, the movement was in a large part directed against British industry. British goods were burned in public and Gandhi campaigned for the use of the spinning wheel as a way of keeping production in the hands of Indian workers.

Gandhi united members of all classes against the foreign capitalists and many were expelled, but Indian capitalists proved just as capable of exploiting Indians as foreigners had been.

Although his movement was non-violent, Gandhi's religious nationalism appealed mainly to Hindus and his vigorous opposition to left wing groups advocating working class unity eventually contributed to the violent Hindu-Moslem conflict.

Although India is now one of the world's leading industrial countries, its workers are rated, along with those in South East Asia, as among its poorest.

141

UNITE!

Anti-imperialist struggles are a fight against the same economic system (multinational companies, banks and money markets) that exploit workers in the West. Unfortunately, workers' movements and national liberation struggles are seldom linked.

*SEE P.89

143

In the 1920s Lenin argued that industrial workers, as a class, were the only people capable of overthrowing capitalism as a world system. He contrasted them with peasants, trapped in isolated units of production and lacking the material base to form a society free from want. Industrial workers alone, Lenin asserted, have the independence, collective force and productive capacity to create the surplus wealth necessary for socialism. Hence they should form an alliance with national liberation movements and wage a united battle against imperialism.

Trotsky went further. Such an alliance would only be effective if from the beginning socialists organised against the middle-class leadership of liberation movements to ensure that the struggle is continued after independence, until socialism is achieved.

Faced with the indifference and even racism of white workers, and besieged by poverty, famine and extreme exploitation as their countries began to industrialise, socialists in Third World countries became disillusioned with such strategies. They searched for roads to socialism independent of white workers and western socialists. For many, **Maoism** seemed to be the answer.

Maoism – 'Mao Tse Tung Thought' adapted the ideas of Marx and Lenin and made them more attractive to Third World socialists. Mao himself even warned against the uncritical acceptance of Marxism, reminding people that it was 'a piece of western culture'.

Mao's ideas appealed to people in developing countries with large peasant populations because he stressed the revolutionary role of the peasantry – 'the people' – rather than the working class. The downplaying of workers' part in revolutions was not just rhetoric; it applied in practice too.

Workers played a secondary role in Mao's revolution, which had been led by a guerilla army.

When the armies marched into the cities, workers were not urged to take over their factories but were instructed instead to stay at their work benches and obey their managers. Mao's brand of socialism stressed the need for hard work and co-operation between classes in order to cut costs and boost production.

Impressive material gains resulted, including the elimination of starvation. But economic pressures meant that democracy was in short supply. All those who opposed the many twists and turns in government policy as China strove to survive within the world economic system were suppressed.

Militia women training.

Not surprisingly, many early admirers lost faith with Maoism as the Chinese government adapted domestic and foreign policy in order to survive, and the dream of socialism was replaced by purges, prison camps, show trials and murders. In December 1984, the Chinese Communist Party finally announced that China was turning away from marxism and adopting a more pragmatic approach. The new policy is summed up by the government slogan, 'It doesn't matter if a cat is black or white as long as it catches mice.'

GUERRILLAS

Guerrilla warfare is now most commonly associated with its most romantic exponent, **Che Guevara**, who played a prominent role in the Cuban revolution of 1959. Guevara argued that it was not necessary to wait until conditions were ripe for proletarian revolution; a small guerrilla band could lead an insurrection by gradually gaining popular support against the ruling class.

Like Maoism, the guerrilla strategies stress revolutionary initiative rather than the need to organize industrial workers. Even where guerrilla movements have been based in cities, they act in place of workers instead of in alliance with them.

Guevara's plans to 'export' the Cuban revolution to other Latin American countries consisted chiefly of training guerrilla armies, which would remain in isolated rural bases until they had popular support. In practice, Guevara always failed to win local workers and peasants to his cause. He was killed in the jungles of Bolivia in 1967.

The Tupamaros guerrillas of Uruguay specialised in kidnapping foreign businessmen. Their spectacular tactics gained them many admirers in the 1960s, but their actions provoked massive repression from the state. In 1972, a thousand were arrested by the Uruguayan army and the movement has never really recovered. Armed attacks in Ireland have been similarly unsuccessful. In Africa guerrilla movements have achieved more because they were accompanied by strikes and unrest among industrial workers, as in Kenya, Mozambique, Tanzania and Zimbabwe.

THE PEASANTS ARE THE MOST WRETCHED AND SO THE MOST REVOLUTIONARY! AND THEY'LL GET NO HELP FROM ANY WEALTHY WESTERNERS!

Although socialism has not materialized in China, Mao's use of a guerrilla army as a base for building socialism has inspired many to use similar tactics.

149

IMPERIALISM AND WAR

Individual capitalists are often greedy and racist, but imperialism itself is not the result of the greed and racism of individual capitalists. It is a logical consequence of the development of capitalism once it has reached certain levels of production.

As Lenin explained:

"The capitalists partition the world not out of personal malice, but because the degree of concentration which has been reached forces them to adopt this method in order to get more profits."

Capitalist expansion necessarily leads to military confrontation between rival states; they are two sides of the same coin.

Two world wars resulted from such conflicts. Since the last world war and the Yalta agreement, which cynically parcelled out the world to different powers, the world has become increasingly split into two opposing camps.

In the boom years of the immediate post-war period, the arrangement seemed almost stable. The Western powers formed overlapping economic, military and political alliances with each other, whilst the most powerful, the USA, began a massive arms build up to discourage interference from the other camp. In the East, Russia consolidated its sphere of influence in Eastern Europe and, through judicious support of national liberation struggles, gained markets in Africa.

While both Russia and America enjoyed high growth rates they moved towards *détente* (peaceful co-existence) and tried very hard not to tread on each other's toes. America confined herself to verbal abuse when the tanks rolled into Budapest in 1956 and Prague in 1968 to smash workers who called for democracy and freedom. For her part, Russia merely remonstrated when the American government bombed Hanoi and spread napalm across the Vietnamese countryside.

The economic crisis of the 70s has changed the

relationship. Both superpowers have built up a massive military machine, but their hold on their own camps is slipping. The struggle of the Polish workers in 1980 and the increasing integration of East European economies with those of the West show Russia's weakening grip on her empire. Events in Nicaragua and El Salvador indicate a similar loosening of US control. The superpowers have gone to enormous lengths to prevent defection from their camps, but without really solving the problem. In Poland a military coup master-minded from Moscow smashed the 10 million strong Solidarity union but has not been able to restore industrial or social 'peace'.

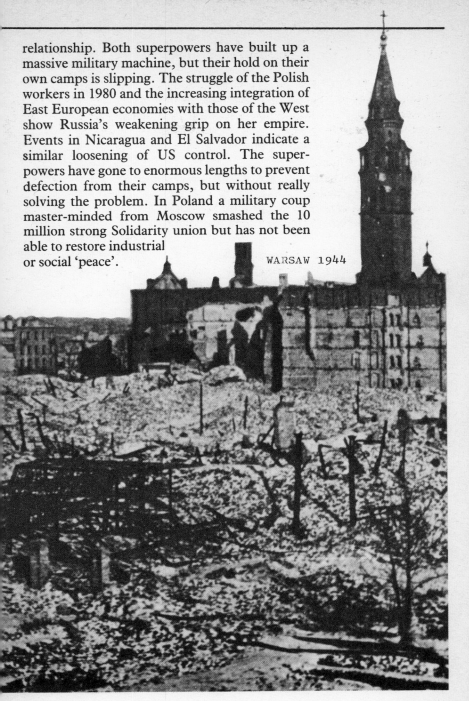

WARSAW 1944

In Nicaragua the US has tried four years of economic blockade and war in order to wreck the advances made by the country's revolutionary leaders. **Ronald Reagan** spends millions of dollars every year arming counter-revolutionary groups, but the Nicaraguan government of the Sandinistas still won a landslide victory in the 1984 elections.

The instability within the two camps has led to increasing aggression. This has led to a spiral of arms spending so immense that it is increasingly alienating those whom it is supposed to protect.

...thin their jungle hideouts, the Contras ...etic image. Starved of American back- ...d last year to cut off funds and harrassed ...Sandinista forces, the surviving guer ...prospect of overturning the left-wing ...hopes must lie in the intensive politica ...Washington this mon...

Longing won't bring him back sooner...
GET A WAR JOB!
SEE YOUR U. S. EMPLOYMENT SERVICE

THE PEACE MOVEMENT

In Britain the peace movement started early. From 1958 to 1962 a popular movement united round the call for unilateral disarmament and mobilised tens of thousands of people on demonstrations outside military bases. At one time this movement even won the majority of the British Labour Party (though this decision was soon reversed, partly by the opposition of most of the big trade unions). Support faded after the Nuclear Test Ban Treaty was signed between Russia, Britain and America (1963). Apart from Japan, where there has been persistent opposition to nuclear weapons, there was no other mass peace movement until the 1980s.

Developments in the West were paralleled by the growth of independent peace groups in Eastern Europe. In Hungary the Dialogue group was formed; in East Germany a group was built whose symbol was 'Swords into Ploughshares' and even in Russia itself organizations opposed to militarism have begun. Small and immediately repressed by the state authorities, they nevertheless show that, East and West, more and more people are mobilising against the nuclear threat.

No movements grew during the period of *détente* between the superpowers, which encouraged the belief that a nuclear war had become less likely. But the peace movement emerged again on a wide scale after 1980 and the start of the second Cold War. In the autumn of 1981 two and half million people in Europe demonstrated their opposition to nuclear weapons. In June 1982 hundreds of thousands of Americans gathered in New York to show their opposition to their government's policy. A majority of British trade unions became affiliated to the Campaign for Nuclear Disarmament (CND). Then in December 1982, the 50,000 women who demonstrated outside the American airbase at Greenham in Britain inspired the setting up of similar 'peace camps' all over Europe.

Richard Stewart

Their concern springs from several sources. First, new intermediate and long-range missiles are being introduced: Cruise and Pershing by the NATO forces and SS20s by Russia. Second, the world economic crisis has provoked greater East-West tension than before over eruptions within each world camp. Events in Afghanistan, Angola, Central America and Iran have been accompanied by tough foreign policy stands from the American government matched by equally aggressive statements from Russia.

The peace movement is a reaction not only to current events in the world. It also has roots deep in the history of the post-war left.

THE NEW LEFT

The New Left developed mainly among students, and arose at a time when the workers' movement internationally was at a very low ebb. Inside the colleges it challenged the outmoded academic syllabuses. Outside, it concentrated on support for liberation struggles – particularly that of the Vietnamese against American imperialism.

In America it grew out of the fight for civil rights and resulted in the formation of the famous but shortlived SDS – Students for a Democratic Society – some of whose members later went underground to engage in acts of terrorism.

The student left turned its back on working class organization. In France, a tendency led by **Daniel Cohn Bendit,** even rejected all existing workers' organisations. For them, trade unions were a reactionary force which simply integrated workers into the capitalist system.

THE EVENTS OF 1968

The events of 1968 forced student radicals to develop a wider perspective. 1968 was a year of revolution internationally. Students protested against Russian domination in Czechoslovakia and Poland, and a civil rights movement was founded in Northern Ireland. In China, the Red Guards of Mao's Cultural Revolution apparently purged the old leaders and old ideas. In Vietnam the successful Tet Offensive by the Vietcong in the spring led to a euphoric belief in the power of student protest among Western supporters of liberation struggles. Students took to the streets of Chicago, Berlin, London and Paris. In America, black people followed suit with massive riots in Detroit. In May the French student protest sparked action by 11 million French workers, who staged a general strike. This re-emergence of workers as an organized social force took everybody by surprise, and put the issue of working-class socialism back on the agenda.

Many searched for working class parties to join. But the traditional workers' parties, the Communist parties, were further discredited in the summer of 1968 when Russian tanks invaded Czechoslovakia and put a brutal end to the Prague Spring. Thousands streamed out of the Western Communist Parties to join those who had left when the Hungarian revolution was similarly crushed in 1956.

Disaffection with Moscow-based socialism led to a small, but significant, revival of other left tendencies. Trotsky's ideas were taken out of obscurity, dusted down and reactivated. They formed a distinct anti-Stalinist current in all Western countries. Maoism also became popular.

Others went further down the sectional road – notably black radicals and feminists. Both grew out of the civil rights movements in America in the 1960s.

BLACK LIBERATION

The movement for black civil rights was a pacifist movement led in America by clergyman **Martin Luther King.** Its aim of integration and equality through peaceful civil disobedience was challenged by black nationalism, whose activists argued for a separate black development based on businesses run by blacks, and the adoption of a non-white religion – Islam.

The best-known orator of the 'Black Muslims', **Malcolm X**, was moving towards a kind of socialism before he was murdered in 1965.

The Civil Rights movement failed, and Martin Luther King was assassinated in 1968. But the movement raised aspirations of young black people. Riots occurred in black ghettoes all over America. In their wake, the Black Panthers took over the leadership of the Black movement.

Unlike some others in the 'Black Power' movement, Black Panthers said capitalism was not a 'white' system but a class system and should be fought by both oppressed blacks and oppressed whites. They wanted organisation to replace spontaneous riots and claimed the right to carry arms as self-defence against racists and the police. They criticised the black groups who looked to liberation through separate development or the revival of black culture, and urged black people to learn to use modern technology rather than look backward to tribalism.

The imagination and daring of the Panthers attracted a wide, militant following among black youth. It also earned them the opposition of the American state. In a few years imprisonment, assassination and police-provoked gun battles entirely eliminated the Panther leadership.

AFRO HAIRDOS WON'T OVERTHROW THE STATE: WE MUST USE MODERN TECHNOLOGY AND INDUSTRIAL MUSCLE — TRIBALISM ISN'T GOING TO DO IT!

THESE PANTHERS ARE A DANGER TO THE MINDS AND SOFT WHITE FLESH OF OUR CHILDREN GO OUT AND KILL THEM SERGEANT.

MY PLEASURE SIR!

JUST GET 'EM OFF THE STREETS ANY WAY YOU CAN

WOMEN'S LIBERATION

Women's liberation also grew up in America, among the thousands of women who entered higher education in the 1960s.

 The growth of the movement was spurred by the so-called 'revolutions' in household technology and contraception, which promised to liberate women from housework and constant childbearing. The movement did not confine itself to demanding equal rights. Child care, housework, sex and lifestyles all became political issues too. The movement began in America but rapidly spread to all Western countries. The upheaval among middle class women was matched by equal pay strikes and a massive increase in trade union membership among women workers. The movement found an echo in Eastern Europe. In 1977 the first feminist underground journal, *Women and Russia* – a fierce attack on the way women in Russia are treated – was produced by a group of women in Leningrad.

In the West, different strategies emerged.

Separatists rejected everything male; socialist-feminists wanted democracy and equality for all, a view epitomised by the statement 'the women question is the whole people question'. What united the movement was the stress on the need for women to organise themselves. The British feminist **Sheila Rowbotham** expressed that need when she wrote:

> "It is only when women start to organize together in large numbers that we begin to become a political force and begin to move toward the possibility of a truly democratic society."

WHATEVER HAPPENED TO THE LEFT?

The emphasis on self-activity and self-organization was vital. Feminism revived the 'woman question', a tradition that had been ignored by socialists for years. The slogan 'The Personal is Political' broadened the struggle for freedom and socialism by emphasising that capitalism has to be resisted not only at work but in every part of our lives. Women's liberation has become an integral part of socialism.

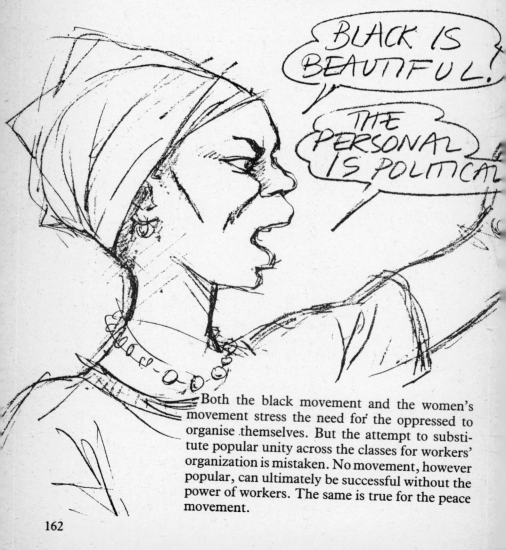

Both the black movement and the women's movement stress the need for the oppressed to organise themselves. But the attempt to substitute popular unity across the classes for workers' organization is mistaken. No movement, however popular, can ultimately be successful without the power of workers. The same is true for the peace movement.

In Europe in the 1980s, the peace movement has attracted many socialists in the same way that the solidarity campaigns in support of the National Liberation Front in Vietnam did during the late 1960s. Nuclear disarmament has become a rallying point for socialists, among others, not because its policies are revolutionary (they are not) but because left parties in general have so little credibility.

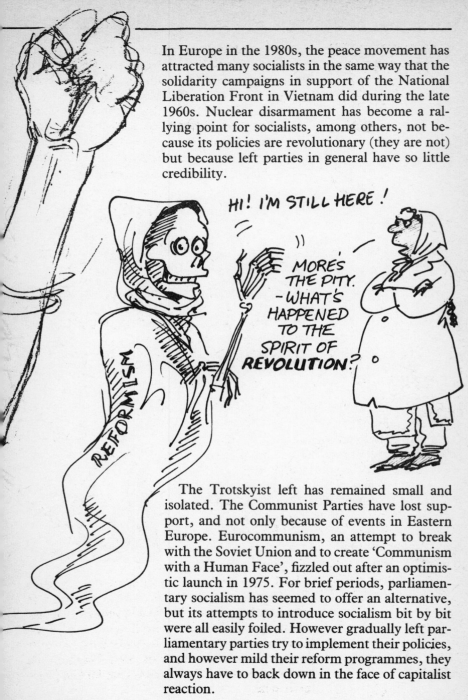

The Trotskyist left has remained small and isolated. The Communist Parties have lost support, and not only because of events in Eastern Europe. Eurocommunism, an attempt to break with the Soviet Union and to create 'Communism with a Human Face', fizzled out after an optimistic launch in 1975. For brief periods, parliamentary socialism has seemed to offer an alternative, but its attempts to introduce socialism bit by bit were all easily foiled. However gradually left parliamentary parties try to implement their policies, and however mild their reform programmes, they always have to back down in the face of capitalist reaction.

163

HELLO – I'M YOUR LOCAL LABOUR – SORRY – I MEAN **BANK OF ENGLAND** – CANDIDATE!

Reaction often takes the form of extreme financial pressure, as happened to the 1964 Labour Government in Britain. Prime Minister **Harold Wilson** was elected to power after 13 years of Tory rule. His policies were scarcely revolutionary, but still they were too radical for the financiers. As he explained in his memoirs:

"The Governor of the Bank of England became a frequent visitor... we had to listen night after night to demands that there should be immediate cuts in Government expenditure... Not for the first time, I said we had now reached the situation where a newly elected government with a mandate from the people was being told, not so much by the Governor of the Bank of England but by international speculators, that the policies on which we had fought the election could not be implemented."

Harold Wilson.

The British Labour Party wasn't the only victim. In 1981, **François Mitterrand's** socialist government in France suffered in a similar way. Money poured out of the country when he was elected, and a severe financial crisis developed as Mitterrand tried to implement a programme of extensive nationalisation.

If economic power is not enough to halt socialism, then more extreme measures are resorted to.

In 1973 a left-wing government was elected in Chile. Its leader, **Salvador Allende**, cut rents and US copper firms were nationalised. To speed up nationalisation, workers began to take matters into their own hands.

Many more *cordones* (workers' committees) have been organised until now they dominate all access roads to the capital. In response to instruction from the labour leadership, the workers have occupied about one hundred factories, most of which are now being run by the unions.

THE GUARDIAN

ALLENDE AND 'POPULAR UNITY' OPPOSED FACTORY OCCUPATIONS AND FORCED THE WORKERS TO DISARM...

Allende and his government opposed the development of independent workers' committees. They persuaded workers to disarm and let the government look after their interests instead. This proved disastrous. In 1974 a US-backed military coup overthrew Allende. Tens of thousands of socialists were exiled, imprisoned, tortured or murdered.

The coup in Chile showed once again how the international ruling class will go to any lengths to maintain its power.

I THINK I SEE THE END OF THE PARLIAMENTARY ROAD, SALVADOR!

IF ONLY...

HISTORICAL EVENTS HAVE REPEATEDLY SHOWN HOW SOCIALISM CAN ONLY BE WON BY WORKERS ORGANIZING THEMSELVES DEMOCRATICALLY FROM BELOW!

The importance of an independent workers' **organization** for resisting such pressures was shown clearly in Portugal in 1974. When fascist rule ended on the death of the dictator, **Antonio Salazar**, there was a revolutionary upsurge: peasants occupied the land and formed co-operatives, workers elected councils at their workplaces, and a widespread process of *saneamento* (cleansing) removed many right-wingers from office in public institutions. But no independent workers' party emerged, mainly because people expected the Movement of Armed Forces, the liberal wing of the army, to defend them.

THERE'S NO POINT IN WAITING FOR THE IDEAL SITUATION TO START FIGHTING FROM — YOU CAN'T PICK YOUR BATTLE-GROUND

BUT WE CAN'T FIGHT BACK ONE AT A TIME — WE NEED A PARTY!

When the government came under international financial pressure to make Portuguese capitalism efficient and competitive, it turned its back on the workers, rallied support on the right and disbanded the liberal wing of the army. Workers had no organization of their own to fight for them, and the revolution died.

WHAT NEXT?

The peace movement has united many shades of opinion against the threat of nuclear war. But the pacifist politics of the mainstream of the movement are not equal to the enormity of the task. Revolutionary socialists have always stressed that militarism and war cannot be ended without the defeat of their root cause – capitalism. Capitalism is a world system and all the struggles against it are interlinked. To be successful they must be united. At present there are people fighting the evils of capitalism all over the world. But we are disunited, like an army that has been told to 'Charge – but one at a time, and only when you feel like it.' We rarely fight back together.

There have been brief examples of international unity. At the end of the First World War workers rose up all over Europe, although only Russian workers achieved a successful revolution. In 1936 the Republican struggle in Spain united workers from many different countries in the struggle against Fascism.

More recently, 10 million Polish workers formed Solidarity and inspired workers on the other side of the world. Striking Zambian miners carried 'Solidarity' placards and explicitly compared their situation with that of Polish workers; Mirafiori car workers in Italy occupied their factory against unemployment emphasising that they were using the same tactics as those used by Polish workers. In São Paulo, labour leader **Ignacio da Silva** became known as 'the **Lech Walesa** of Brazil'.

WE ARE BACK WHERE WE STARTED AS AN ORGANISATION— OPPOSING THOSE IN POWER ABOUT THE ONLY THING WE HAVEN'T GOT IN COMMON WITH POLISH MINERS IS THE RUSSIANS BREATHING DOWN OUR BACKS!

CAMERAPIX

Such unity is only born out of action. Four hundred years ago, the English revolutionary Gerrard Winstanley knew this:

"Everyone talks of freedom, but there are few that act for freedom, and the actors for freedom are oppressed by the talkers and the verbal professors of freedom."

170

Three hundred years later his words and actions were echoed by **Frederick Douglass,** an escaped slave active in the abolition movement:

> "The whole history of the progress of human liberty shows that all concessions made to her august claims have been born of struggle. If there is no struggle, there is no progress."

Struggle is the lifeblood of socialism.

Organization is essential also. Recognising this fact, Marx worked within the International Working Men's Association to unite the leaders of working class struggles. Today no such international organization of socialists exists. History has left us democratic models, imperfect but inspiring: the Paris Commune, the Russian soviets, and Polish Solidarity. There are no blueprints for the kind of organization we need. Different circumstances require different kinds of organizations. We do know that socialism can only be built by workers. Rosa Luxemburg put it bluntly:

FREEDOM!

> "Socialism must be created by the masses, by every proletarian. Where the chains of capitalism are forged, there must they be broken."

Socialism is workers' power.

Of course to lay stress on the role of workers does not mean that socialists should limit their activity to struggles in the workplace. Socialism is broader than that. Socialists should fight in every arena. Capitalism affects every part of our lives. The fights against sexism and racism, the peace and ecology movements, the national liberation struggles are all vital parts of the struggle for socialism. They strengthen socialism.

— AND HERRINGS TOO!

'In the phraseology of politics, a party too indifferent to the sorrow and sufferings of humanity to raise its voice in protest, is a moderate, practical party; whilst a party totally indifferent to the personality of leaders, or questions of leadership, but not to enthusiasm on every question affecting the well-being of the toiling masses, is an extreme, a dangerous party.'

James Connolly (1870-1916)

We socialists are feminists, peaceniks, ecologists and liberationists not just out of principle but because it makes us stronger; more dangerous. If we want to overthrow the existing society, we've got to be dangerous, we've got to be organized and we've got to use our power as workers.

Freedom is a powerful idea. Since the beginning of class society people have dreamed of, and fought for, freedom. Now industrial workers as a class have the potential to make that dream a reality.

Socialists are always being told: 'It's all right in theory but it will never work.' There's only one answer to that. *Go out and organize.* Prove it is possible.

"Revolution is never practical – until the hour of revolution strikes. Then it alone is practical and all the efforts of the conservatives and compromisers become the most futile and visionary of human imaginings."
James Connolly

the End.

APPENDIX

Where did the red flag come from?

Socialism is often associated with the red flag. Why?

It was already being used by workers as a symbol of resistance in 1797. Sailors on the Royal Navy flag ship, the *Queen Charlotte*, mutinied in Portsmouth harbour. During their strike, they hoisted the red flag – the signal which means 'attack'. The Admiral of the Fleet eventually agreed to meet their demands, but their leader, **Valentine Joyce**, warned them to "Remember the *Culloden*." (A ship on which men had mutinied, apparently successfully. After they had returned to work, the authorities hanged ten of their leaders.)

Valentine Joyce insisted that the men demand an Act of Parliament, passed by both Houses, guaranteeing no victimisation, before they would return to work. The situation in the navy was so desperate that the Act was passed in 48 hours, with Prime Minister **William Pitt** having to bully the King of England, **George III**, into signing. Over 180 such mutinies occurred in **Lord Nelson's** navy alone.

But that wasn't the very first time that the red flag was seen. It had already been used in the 1760s, hoisted by female pirates when they set up communes in the West Indies. People usually think that the pirate flag is black and white – the 'skull and crossbones'. But the usual name for it, 'Jolly Roger', is not an English name at all, but a perversion of the French '*Jolie Rougier*' (red and beautiful).

BOOKS

The following are some of the books I used when I was writing *Socialism*. The list is not meant to be exhaustive. It indicates those books I found most interesting and most enjoyable (A.P.)

Manifesto of the Communist Party by Marx and Engels. Many editions, including Progress Publishers: Moscow.
Begin here with the original case for socialism from below.

The Age of Revolution by E.J. Hobsbawm. Sphere Books 1977.
Marxist account of 'the transformation of the world between 1789 and 1848'.

A People's History of England by A.L. Morton. Lawrence and Wishart 1976.
History of England from Stone Age to 1918.

The British Labour Movement by A.L. Morton and George Tate. Lawrence and Wishart 1979.
Easy to read history of the world's first working class.

The English Utopia by A.L. Morton. Lawrence and Wishart 1978.
Dreams of a better world from the poor (Cockaygne) and the rich (Utopia).

Ideology and Popular Protest by George Rudé. Lawrence and Wishart 1980.
Exciting account of lesser known riots and rebellions in Europe.

Karl Marx's Theory of Revolution. (2 volumes) by Hal Draper. Monthly Review Press 1977.
Highly recommended for anyone who wants a detailed introduction to Marx without headaches.

Marxism and Freedom by Raya Dunayevskaya. Pluto Press 1971.
Humanist case for marxism. Wonderful.

Ten Days That Shook The World by John Reed. Penguin 1970.
Forget 'Reds', just read the book. An exciting first hand account of Russia 1917.

Midnight in the Century by Victor Serge. Writers and Readers, 1984.
Poetic and moving novel, based on fact, about the failure of the workers' revolution in Russia.
Other Victor Serge novels and his autobiography, *Memoirs of a Revolutionary*, deal with different aspects of the same event and are well worth reading.

The Mandate of Heaven – Marx and Mao in Modern China by Nigel Harris. Quartet Books 1978.
Explains why China isn't socialist.

Revolution and Bureaucracy in Eastern Europe by Chris Harman. Pluto Press 1974.
Post war history of workers' movements in Eastern Europe. Explains that what calls itself 'socialism' is actually state capitalism.

The Black Jacobins by C.L.R. James. Vintage Books 1963 and *This Gilded African – Toussaint L'Ouverture* by Wenda Parkinson. Quartet Books 1980.
Two exciting accounts of slave revolts in the West Indies. The first is a socialist 'classic'.

Striking Against Apartheid by John Rogers. Socialists Unlimited 1982.
Brief, exciting account of workers' struggle against imperialism in Africa.

The Women Incendiaries by Ruth Thomas. Secker and Warburg 1966.
The story of women in the Paris Commune.

Women, Resistance and Revolution by Sheila Rowbotham. Penguin 1972.
Covers the often overlooked part that women have played in revolutionary movements.

The Second Cold War by Fred Halliday. Verso Books 1983.
A clear and interesting analysis of the basis of conflicts between Russia and America since 1945.

Of Bread and Guns by Nigel Harris. Pelican Books 1983.
Socialist analysis of the world economy which shows how defence spending, social services and other economic elements are linked.

Marxism and the Party by John Molyneux. Pluto Press 1978.
Tells you how socialists have organized in the past and why workers need a party to win.

INDEX OF NAMES